Functional Skills

Maths

Edexcel – Entry Level 3

This brilliant CGP book is the best way to prepare for Edexcel Entry Level 3 Functional Skills Maths. It covers everything you need... and nothing you don't!

Every topic is clearly explained, along with all the non-calculator methods you'll need for the latest exam. There are practice questions throughout the book <u>and</u> a realistic practice paper at the end — all with answers included.

How to access your free Online Edition

This book includes a free Online Edition to read on your PC, Mac or tablet. You'll just need to go to **cgpbooks.co.uk/extras** and enter this code:

0828 3384 2176 0442

By the way, this code only works for one person. If somebody else has used this book before you, they might have already claimed the Online Edition.

CGP — still the best! ☺

Our sole aim here at CGP is to produce the highest quality books — carefully written, immaculately presented and dangerously close to being funny.

Then we work our socks off to get them out to you — at the cheapest possible prices.

Contents

Section Three — Handling Data

Published by CGP

Editors:
Adam Bartlett, Michael Bushell, Caley Simpson, Michael Weynberg

With thanks to Tom Miles and David Norden for the proofreading.

ISBN: 978 1 78908 389 7

Printed by Elanders Ltd, Newcastle upon Tyne.
Clipart from Corel®

Numbers

All Numbers are Made of Digits

1) A digit is just one of these:

   0   1   2   3   4   5   6   7   8   9

2) All numbers are made by putting these digits together.

3) For example, 21, 48, 321 or 648.

Two-digit Numbers

The first digit of a two-digit number tells you how many tens the number has.

The second digit tells you how many units (ones) the number has.

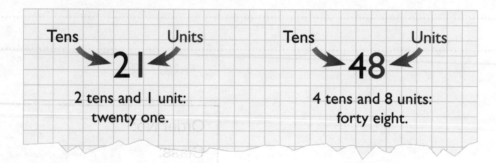

Tens   Units
21
2 tens and 1 unit:
twenty one.

Tens   Units
48
4 tens and 8 units:
forty eight.

Three-digit Numbers

The first digit of a three-digit number tells you how many hundreds the number has.

The second digit tells you how many tens the number has.

The third digit tells you how many units the number has.

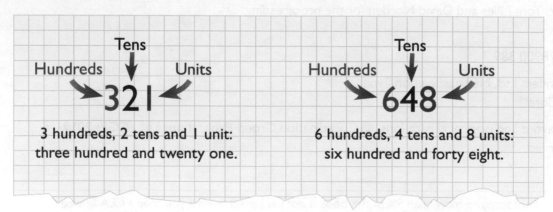

Hundreds   Tens   Units
321
3 hundreds, 2 tens and 1 unit:
three hundred and twenty one.

Hundreds   Tens   Units
648
6 hundreds, 4 tens and 8 units:
six hundred and forty eight.

Finding the Lowest Number From the First Digit

1) First, find the numbers with the fewest digits.

2) From these, the one with the lowest first digit is the lowest number.

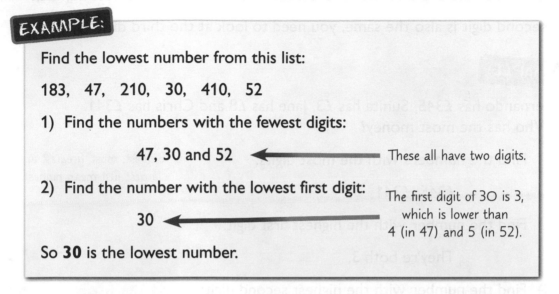

EXAMPLE:

Find the lowest number from this list:

183, 47, 210, 30, 410, 52

1) Find the numbers with the fewest digits:

   47, 30 and 52 ⟵ These all have two digits.

2) Find the number with the lowest first digit:

   30 ⟵ The first digit of 30 is 3, which is lower than 4 (in 47) and 5 (in 52).

So **30** is the lowest number.

3) If the first digits are the same, you'll have to look at the other digits — this is shown on the next page.

Finding the Highest Number From the First Digit

1) First, find the numbers with the most digits.

2) From these, the one with the highest first digit is the highest number.

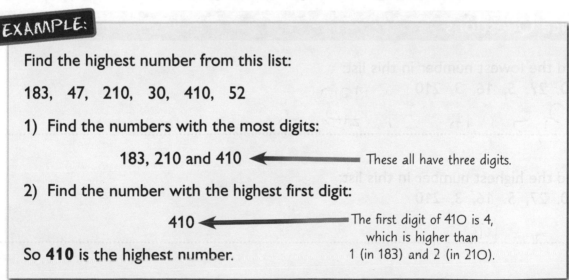

EXAMPLE:

Find the highest number from this list:

183, 47, 210, 30, 410, 52

1) Find the numbers with the most digits:

   183, 210 and 410 ⟵ These all have three digits.

2) Find the number with the highest first digit:

   410 ⟵ The first digit of 410 is 4, which is higher than 1 (in 183) and 2 (in 210).

So **410** is the highest number.

3) If the first digits are the same, you'll have to look at the other digits — this is shown on the next page.

Finding Highest and Lowest Numbers Using the Other Digits

1) If two numbers have the same number of digits, and their first digit is the same, you need to look at the second digit. The one with the highest second digit is the highest number and the one with the lowest second digit is the lowest number.

2) If the second digit is also the same, you need to look at the third digit.

EXAMPLE:

Fernando has £345, Sunita has £3, Jane has £8 and Chris has £341.
Who has the most money?

1) Find the numbers with the most digits:

£345, £341

Biggest, most, greatest and largest just mean highest.

2) Find the number with the highest first digit:

They're both 3.

3) Find the number with the highest second digit:

They're both 4.

4) Find the number with the highest third digit:

£345 ⟵ *The third digit of 345 is 5, which is higher than the third digit of 341 (which is 1).*

So **Fernando** has the most money.

Practice Questions

1) Find the lowest number in this list:
190, 27, 5, 16, 3, 210

3, 5, 16, 27, 210, 190

2) Find the highest number in this list:
190, 27, 5, 16, 3, 210

3, 5 190

3) Phil has 6 days of holiday left, Colm has 14, Dorothy has 17 and Jacinta has 2.
Who has the most days of holiday left?

Putting Numbers in Order

1) First, sort the numbers into groups with the same number of digits. The numbers with the most digits are the largest and the numbers with the fewest digits are the smallest

2) Then put the numbers in each group in order. Start by looking at the first digit.

3) If the first digits are the same, move onto the second digit, then the third digit.

EXAMPLE:

Aki has six screws of different lengths:
109 mm, 9 mm, 38 mm, 64 mm, 125 mm, 32 mm.
Put the screws in order of length from largest to smallest.

1) Put the lengths into groups. The ones with the most digits should go into the first group.

3 digits	2 digits	1 digit
109 mm, 125 mm	38 mm, 64 mm, 32 mm	9 mm

2) Put the numbers in each separate group in order of size from largest to smallest.

125 mm, 109 mm   64 mm, 38 mm, 32 mm   9mm

3) So the lengths in order from largest to smallest are:

125 mm, 109 mm, 64 mm, 38 mm, 32 mm, 9 mm

Practice Questions

1) Put these numbers in order from smallest to largest:
26, 27, 4, 7, 129, 37, 136

_4, 7, 26, 27, 37, 129, 136_

2) The table below shows how much money five people have in their bank accounts.

Sarah	£24
Heather	£473
Rina	£254
Katie	£52
Jane	£5

Put the names in order from the person with the most money in their bank account to the person with the least money in their bank account.

_£473 £254, £52, £24, £5_

Adding and Subtracting

You Need to Know When to Add

1) The questions you get in the test will be based on real-life situations.

2) You won't always be told what calculation to do to answer the question.

3) You'll need to work out for yourself what calculation to do.

4) Sometimes it will involve adding numbers together.

5) Addition is shown by a + sign.

EXAMPLE 1:

Charlene is ordering some tickets online.
The costs of the tickets, booking fee and delivery are shown below.

How much will one ticket cost her in total if she picks it up herself?

Ticket	£12
Booking fee	£2
Delivery	£3

Answer: you need to add together the price of a ticket plus the booking fee. You don't need to add on the delivery fee because Charlene is picking up the ticket herself. So the calculation you need to do is:

$$12 + 2 = £14$$

Sometimes you need to include units in your answer. Units tell you what type of number you've got. In this case the units are pounds, '£'.

EXAMPLE 2:

Asha is cleaning her house. How long it takes to clean each room is shown below. How long does it take to clean all the rooms?

Kitchen, 2 hours	Dining room, 1 hour
Living room, 2 hours	Bathroom, 1 hour

Answer: you need to add together the times for all the rooms.
So the calculation you need to do is:

$$2 + 1 + 2 + 1 = 6 \text{ hours}$$ ← The units here are 'hours'.

You Need to Know When to Subtract

1) Sometimes you'll need to subtract — take one number away from another.

2) Subtraction is shown using a – sign.

EXAMPLE 1:

Warren is paying for some crisps. The crisps cost £2.
He pays with a £10 note. How much change should he get back?

Answer: you need to take away how much the crisps cost from how much money he paid with. So the calculation you need to do is:

$$10 - 2 = £8$$

EXAMPLE 2:

Sybil works a 7 hour shift.
Her notes for her time sheet are shown on the right.
How long did she spend packing?

Picking	2 hours
Phones	4 hours
Packing	?

Answer: you need to take away the times you know from the total time she is at work.
So the calculation you need to do is:

$$7 - 2 - 4 = \textbf{1 hour} \text{ is spent packing.}$$

Sometimes there is more than one way to answer a question. For example, here you could have added together the two times you knew (2 + 4 = 6) and then taken that away from 7 (7 – 6 = 1). As long as your method and answer are correct, you'll get the marks.

You Might Need to Add and Subtract

EXAMPLE:

Suri orders salmon and then lemon tart. She has a voucher for £2 off any meal.
How much does she have to pay for her meal?

Answer: this calculation has two steps.

1) Add up the price of the meal: 10 + 4 = 14

2) Then take away the voucher: 14 – 2 = 12

Suri has to pay **£12**.

Salmon	£10
Roast Chicken	£10
Lemon Tart	£4
Cheesecake	£3

You Need to Know How to Add Without Using a Calculator

If you need to add two numbers together but you can't use a calculator, use this method:

1) Write the numbers with one above the other, lining up the units.

2) Add up the columns from right to left. Write the sum at the bottom of each column.

3) If the numbers add up to more than 9, write the units digit at the bottom of the column and 'carry' the 1 to the next column (write a little 1 at the bottom of the next column).

4) Add up each column, including carried numbers. Read the answer from the bottom row.

EXAMPLE:

Molly is furnishing her new home. She buys a sofa that costs £342 and a coffee table which costs £294. What is the total price of the furniture?

Write out the numbers one above the other, lining up the units column. Add up each column in turn, starting with the units column.

$$\begin{array}{r} 342 \\ +294 \\ \hline \end{array}$$
Line up the units.

$$\begin{array}{r} 342 \\ +294 \\ \hline 6 \end{array}$$
$2 + 4 = 6$

$$\begin{array}{r} 342 \\ +294 \\ \hline 36 \\ 1 \end{array}$$
$4 + 9 = 13$. Write the 3 and 'carry' the 1.

$$\begin{array}{r} 342 \\ +294 \\ \hline 636 \\ 1 \end{array}$$
$3 + 2 + \text{carried } 1 = 6$

So the total price is **£636**.

You Need to Know How to Subtract Without Using a Calculator

1) Write the numbers with the bigger one above the smaller one, lining up the units.

2) Working from right to left, starting with the units column, take the bottom number away from the top number.

3) Now subtract the numbers in each column in turn. If the top number in the column is smaller than the bottom number you need to borrow ten from the next column along. To do this, subtract 1 from the column to the left and add 10 to the column you're subtracting.

4) Subtract each column and read the answer from the bottom row.

EXAMPLE:

Ed used to weigh 105 kg and now weighs 91 kg. How much weight has he lost?

Write the bigger number on top of the smaller number and subtract each of the columns in turn from right to left:

Line up the units.
$$\begin{array}{r} 105 \\ -91 \\ \hline \end{array}$$

$5 - 1 = 4$
$$\begin{array}{r} 105 \\ -91 \\ \hline 4 \end{array}$$

$10 - 9 = 1$
$$\begin{array}{r} {}^{0}{}^{10}05 \\ -91 \\ \hline 14 \end{array}$$

O is smaller than 9, so you need to borrow from the hundreds column. This leaves a O in the hundreds column.

Ed has lost **14 kg**.

Using a Calculator

1) Make sure it says '0' before you start.

2) Press the buttons carefully.

3) Always check the display to make sure you've pressed the right button.

4) Press the $=$ button at the end of every calculation.

5) You can add and subtract using a calculator.

EXAMPLE:

James wants to buy a new fridge. One fridge costs £155 and another costs £130. What is the difference in price between the two fridges?

Answer: The calculation you need to do is 155 – 130.

Don't just write down 25 though. You need to think about what the answer on your calculator means and add in any units.

The difference in price is **£25**.

Always Check Your Answer

1) Adding and subtracting are opposite calculations.

2) Once you've got your answer, you can check it using the opposite calculation.

3) You should get back to the number you started with.

EXAMPLE 1:

What is 176 – 12?

Answer: 176 – 12 = **164**

Check it using the opposite calculation: 164 + 12 = 176

You can use a calculator to work this out — but only in the calculator section of the test. To check your answers in the non-calculator section, you'll have to use the methods from the previous page.

EXAMPLE 2:

What is 9 + 15?

Answer: 9 + 15 = **24**

You only need to do one of these calculations to check your answer.

Check it using the opposite calculation: 24 – 9 = 15   OR   24 – 15 = 9

Practice Questions

1) What is 125 + 14?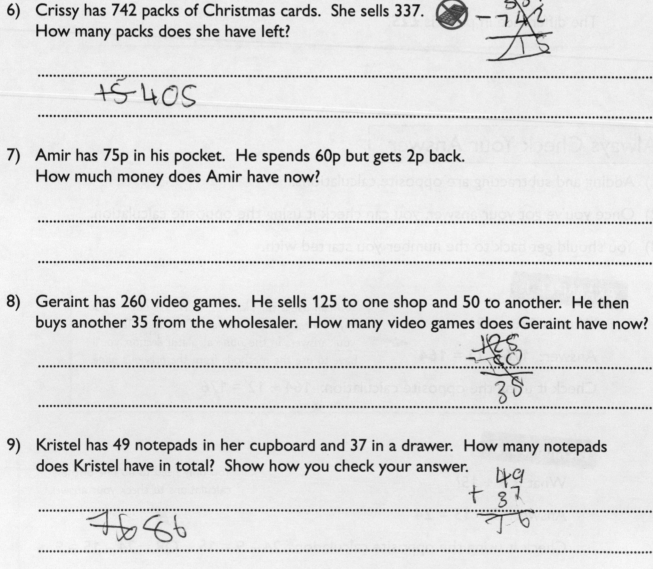

139

2) What is 57 + 74?

131

3) What is 67 − 16?

51

4) What is 176 − 98?

22 78

5) Tristan is buying a Blu-ray player. Model A is £78 and model B is £95. How much more expensive is model B?

6) Crissy has 742 packs of Christmas cards. She sells 337. How many packs does she have left?

405

7) Amir has 75p in his pocket. He spends 60p but gets 2p back. How much money does Amir have now?

8) Geraint has 260 video games. He sells 125 to one shop and 50 to another. He then buys another 35 from the wholesaler. How many video games does Geraint have now?

9) Kristel has 49 notepads in her cupboard and 37 in a drawer. How many notepads does Kristel have in total? Show how you check your answer.

86

Multiplying and Dividing

You Need to Know When to Multiply

1) Some calculations will involve multiplication — one number "times" another.

2) Multiplication is shown using a × sign.

EXAMPLE:

Sharon needs to buy some flour for a cake. A packet of flour costs £2.
Sharon needs 3 packets. How much does the flour cost Sharon in total?

£2 × 3 = **£6**

Multiplying Without a Calculator

1) First, write the numbers with one above the other, with the largest number on the top.
Line up the units.

2) Multiply the units digit of the bottom number by each digit of the top number in turn
(working from right to left) and write the answer at the bottom.

3) If you get an answer of 10 or more, carry the tens digit of the answer to the next column
to the left (like you do when you're adding). Add any carried numbers after doing the
multiplication for the next column.

4) Then multiply the tens digit of the bottom number by each digit of the top number.
You need to add a zero in the units column of the answer as you're multiplying by ten.

5) Finally, add your answers together to get the final answer.

EXAMPLE:

Claude buys a bike. He has to pay £45 a month for 17 months.
How much will Claude pay in total for the bike?

1) First, find 45 × 7.

```
  4 5
× 1 7
  3 1 5
    3
```

7 × 5 = 35,
so put 5 in the
units column and
carry the 3 to
the tens column.

7 × 4 = 28,
28 + carried 3 = 31,
so put 1 in the tens column and
3 in the hundreds column.

2) Then find 45 × 1.

```
  4 5
× 1 7
  3 1 5
  4 5 0
```

When you're multiplying by the tens
digit you need to write a 0 in the
units column. All the other digits
are shifted one column to the left.

3) Add to get the answer.

```
  4 5
× 1 7
  3 1 5
+ 4 5 0
  7 6 5
```

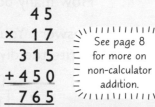
See page 8
for more on
non-calculator
addition.

Claude will pay **£765** in total for the bike.

You Need to Know When to Divide

1) Some calculations will involve division — one number divided by another.

2) Division is shown using a ÷ sign.

> **EXAMPLE:**
>
> Frank drives to work and back 5 days in a row.
> He drives 50 miles in total.
> How many miles does Frank drive each day?
>
> Answer: the 50 miles needs to be divided by 5 days.
> So you need to calculate 50 divided by 5.
>
> $$50 ÷ 5 = \textbf{10 miles} \longleftarrow \text{The units here are 'miles'.}$$

Dividing Without a Calculator

1) Write the small number on the left of the big number.

56 ÷ 4 would be written like this:

4 | 5 6

2) Divide each digit of the bigger number by the small number, working from left to right.

3) Put the result of each division above the big number, lining up the digits.

4) If the number doesn't divide exactly, then the number left over after the division is carried over to the next column. It's then used in the next digit's division (so if a 1 was carried over and the next digit was a 6, 16 would be used for the next division).

5) The amount left over after all the digits have been divided is called the remainder.

> **EXAMPLE:**
>
> Kojo has 158 eggs and wants to put them in boxes of 12.
> How many boxes will he fill and how many eggs will be left over?
>
> Answer: You need to divide 158 by 12.
> Write the division with the small number on the left.
>
>
>
> $$\frac{0}{12\ \overline{\smash{\big|}\ 1^15\ 8}}$$
>
> 12 doesn't go into 1 so carry the 1 over to the next column to the right. Write a 0 on the top.
>
> $$\frac{0\ 1}{12\ \overline{\smash{\big|}\ 1^15^38}}$$
>
> 12 goes into 15 once with 3 left over, so write 1 above the line and carry 3 over.
>
> $$\frac{0\ 1\ 3\ r\ 2}{12\ \overline{\smash{\big|}\ 1^15^38}}$$
>
> 12 goes into 38 three times, so write 3 in the units column.
>
> 12 × 3 = 36
> 38 − 36 = 2, so there is 2 left over. This is the remainder.
>
> So 158 eggs will fill **13 boxes** and Kojo will have **2 eggs** left over.

Multiplying and Dividing with a Calculator

1) You can use a calculator for multiplication and division —
you need to use the ⊠ and ⊟ buttons.

2) Always make sure the screen reads '0' before you start, check the screen
throughout and press the ⊟ button at the end of every calculation.

EXAMPLE:

Lotte has gone out to dinner with 9 friends. The meal costs £280.
The cost will be split equally between Lotte and her friends.
How much will each person pay?

*Equally means everyone
will pay the same amount.*

Answer: Lotte is there with 9 friends, so that's 9 + 1 = 10
people in total. You need to calculate 280 divided by 10.

2 8 0 ÷ 1 0 = 28

280 ÷ 10 = **£28**

Some Questions Need Answers that are Whole Numbers

1) You won't always end up with a whole number when you divide.

2) But sometimes, you'll need to give a whole number as your answer.

EXAMPLE 1:

Camila has 14 large chocolate buttons to give out equally to her 5 students.
How many buttons will each student get?

Calculation: 14 ÷ 5 = 2.8 ←

*Without a calculator,
you'd get 14 ÷ 5 = 2 r 4*

You can't have 2.8 buttons, so the answer needs to be a whole number.

2.8 is between 2 and 3. There aren't enough buttons for 3 each.
So Camila will give each student **2 buttons**.

EXAMPLE 2:

Richard needs 75 chocolate biscuits for a coffee morning.
The biscuits come in packs of 4. How many packs should Richard buy?

Calculation: 75 ÷ 4 = 18.75 ←

*Without a calculator,
you'd get 75 ÷ 4 = 18 r 3*

Richard can't buy 18.75 packs, so your answer needs to be a whole number.

18.75 is between 18 and 19. If Richard buys 18 packs of biscuits,
he won't have enough. So Richard will need to buy **19 packs**.

(handwritten at top of page)

$$\times \begin{array}{r} 35 \\ 4 \\ \hline 120 \end{array}$$

$$\begin{array}{r} .253 \\ \div\ 15 \end{array}$$

Practice Questions

1) What is 35 × 4?

(handwritten) 120
4

2) What is 253 ÷ 15?

(handwritten) 16·8

3) Cassandra is putting out chairs for a concert. There are 126 chairs in total. There need to be exactly 9 chairs in each row. How many rows will there be?

(handwritten) $\times \begin{array}{r} 126 \\ 9 \end{array}$

1134

4) There are 14 screws in a packet. Justin buys 5 packets of screws. He needs 68 screws. Has Justin bought enough screws?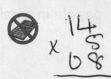

(handwritten) $\times \begin{array}{r} 14 \\ 5 \\ 08 \end{array}$

4700

5) An assistant buys 3 boxes of A3 paper. Each box contains 5 packets. There are 50 sheets of paper in each packet.

a) How many sheets of paper are there in one box?

b) How many sheets of paper has the assistant bought in total?

6) Ki needs to send 27 Christmas cards. The cards she likes come in packs of 5. How many packs should she buy?

(handwritten) $\div \begin{array}{r} 27 \\ 5 \end{array}$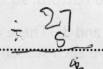

5·4

7) Paula needs 12 daffodils to make a bunch. A customer wants to buy 28 bunches. How many daffodils does she need?

(handwritten) $\times \begin{array}{r} 28 \\ 12 \\ \hline 26 \end{array}$

26

Always Check Your Answer

1) Multiplying and dividing are opposite calculations.

2) Once you've got your answer, you can check it using the opposite calculation.

3) You should get back to the number you started with.

EXAMPLE 1:

What is 137 × 4?

Answer: 137 × 4 = **548**

Check it using the opposite calculation: 548 ÷ 4 = 137   OR   548 ÷ 137 = 4

EXAMPLE 2:

Stella needs 14 fabric heart patches to sew onto some bags.
The hearts are sold in packs of 5. How many packs should Stella buy?

Answer: 14 ÷ 5 = 2.8. Stella will need to buy **3 packs**.

Check it using the opposite calculation:

5 × 2 = 10 (not enough), 5 × 3 = 15 (enough). So Stella must buy 3 packs.

Practice Questions

1) What is 6 × 10? Show how you check your answer.

60 6×10=60 6÷10=1

2) Rachael is pickling eggs. Each jar will hold 5 eggs. Rachael has 125 eggs in total.
How many jars of pickled eggs can she make? Show how you check your answer.

25

3) Himari needs to send 94 invitations in the post. Stamps come in packs of 8.
How many packs of stamps should Himari buy? Show how you check your answer.

752

Rounding

Rounding to the Nearest 10

1) "Rounding to the nearest 10" means finding the nearest number ending in 0.
   For example, 10, 60, 230.

2) If the last digit is less than 5, round down to the ten below.

3) If the last digit is 5 or more, round up to the ten above.

EXAMPLE:

Sam has 32 sandwiches. How many does he have to the nearest 10?

The last digit is 2. This is less than 5, so you need to round it down.

Sam has **30 sandwiches** to the nearest 10.

You can see this on a number line:

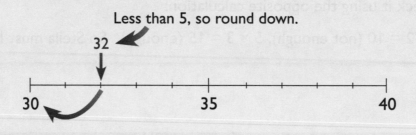

Rounding to the Nearest 100

1) "Rounding to the nearest 100" means finding the nearest number ending in 00.
   For example, 100, 600, 2300.

2) If the last two digits are less than 50, round down to the hundred below.

3) If the last two digits are 50 or more, round up to the hundred above.

EXAMPLE:

Zara has 850 envelopes. How many envelopes
does she have to the nearest hundred?

The last two digits are 50, so round up to the hundred above.

Zara has **900 envelopes** to the nearest hundred.

Practice Questions

1) Tom has 734 red pens.

   a) How many pens does Tom have to the nearest 10?

   730

   b) How many pens does Tom have to the nearest 100?

   ....

2) Alex has 5<u>5</u>0 printers. How many does he have to the nearest 100?

   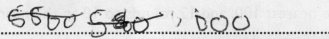

3) Umesh runs 1500 m in 294 seconds.

   a) What is his time to the nearest 100 seconds?

   ....

   b) What is his time to the nearest 10 seconds?

   ....

Estimating Uses Rounding

1) An estimate is a close guess at what an answer will be.

2) You can use rounding to estimate an answer.

EXAMPLE:

Kyle has 32 fairy cakes and 118 cupcakes.
Estimate how many cakes Kyle has in total.

1) First, round both numbers to the nearest 10.

   32 rounds down to 30.

   118 rounds up to 120.

   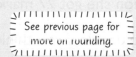
   See previous page for more on rounding.

2) Then add 30 and 120: 30 + 120 = 150

   So Kyle has about **150 cakes** in total.

You can Check your Answer using an Estimate

1) You can also use an estimate to check an answer.

2) The estimate should be close to the exact answer.
   If it isn't, then your answer is probably wrong.

EXAMPLE:

Hyun pays £496 per month in rent. There are 12 months in a year.
Hyun calculates that he will need £59 520 for 1 year of rent.
Use an estimate to check his answer.

1) First, find an estimate for the answer.

   496 rounds to 500 to the nearest 100, and 12 rounds to 10 to the nearest 10.
   £500 × 10 = £5000

2) Compare your estimate to Hyun's answer

   £59 520 is much bigger than £5000, so this suggests Hyun is **incorrect**.

Practice Questions

1) Estimate the answer to 617 + 84.

....

2) Caz is doing some stock taking. She has 98 tins of beans, 45 tins of tomatoes, and 23 tins of spaghetti. Estimate how many tins she has in total.

....

3) Rachel is shopping. She buys food costing £1.99, £2.99, 99p, 99p and £3.99.
   She pays with a £20 note and gets £10.05 change.
   Use an estimate to check if she got the right change.

....

4) Vashti needs a total of 55 marks to pass a test. In the first section she got 34 marks and in the second section she got 27 marks.

   a) Use an estimate to decide if you think she passed or not.

   ....

   b) Vashti calculates that she scored 61 marks. Use your estimate to check her answer.

   ....

Decimals

Not All Numbers Are Whole Numbers

1) Decimals are numbers with a decimal point (.) in them. For example, 0.5, 1.3.

2) If you're saying the number out loud, you say "point" where the "." is.
For example, 1.3 is one point three.

3) They're used to show the numbers in between whole numbers.

4) Digits to the right of the "." are worth less than one.

- The number 0.9 is a bit smaller than the number 1.

- The number 1.1 is a bit bigger than the number 1.

- The number 1.9 is a bit smaller than the number 2.

- The number 1.0 is the same as the number 1.

- The number 1.5 is exactly halfway between the numbers 1 and 2.

- The number 2.54 is bigger than the number 2.51.

- The number 4.61 is smaller than the number 4.63.

- The number 6.80 is exactly the same as the number 6.8.

You Can Show Decimals on a Number Line

1) A number line is a line with numbers spaced out along it in order.

2) The further right a number is on a number line, the bigger it is.

3) The space in between the whole numbers can be split into divisions.

4) If the space is split into 10 divisions then each division is equal to 0.1.

5) You can see this on a number line:

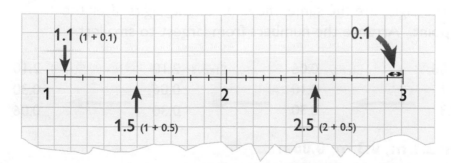

Decimals are Used in Money and Measuring

1) Decimals are used in money to show pounds (£) and pence (p).

2) Money is always written with two digits after the decimal point, even if they're just 0s at the end.

- £7.38 means 7 pounds and 38 pence.
- You write £5.90 not £5.9 for 5 pounds and 90 pence.
- £5.09 is 5 pounds and 9 pence.

3) Decimals are also used in measuring.

4) For example, you can use them to show metres (m) and centimetres (cm).

- 3.20 m means 3 metres and 20 centimetres.
- 3.2 m means 3 m and 20 cm too. ← You don't need to have two digits after the point for measurements.
- 1.62 m means 1 m and 62 cm.

How to Put Decimals in Order

You might need to arrange a list of decimal numbers in order of size.

EXAMPLE:

Put these heights in order of size: 0.06 m, 2.1 m, 0.3 m.
Start with the largest.

1) Put the numbers into a column, lining up the decimal points.

2) Make all the numbers the same length by filling in extra zeros at the ends.

3) Look at the digits before the decimal point. Arrange the numbers from largest to smallest.

4) If any of the digits are the same, move on to the digits after the decimal point. Arrange the numbers from largest to smallest.

Step 1:	Step 2:	Step 3:	Step 4:
0.06	0.06	2.10	2.10
2.1	2.10	0.06	0.30
0.3	0.30	0.30	0.06

The order is: **2.1 m, 0.3 m, 0.06 m**.

Finding the Largest or Smallest Decimal Number

You might need to give the largest or smallest number from a list of decimal numbers.

EXAMPLE:

Jan weighs 75.4 kg, Dylan weighs 52.5 kg and Andy weighs 75.9 kg.
Who weighs the most?

1) Find the number with the highest whole number:
   The numbers with the highest whole numbers are 75.4 kg and 75.9 kg.

2) Look at the first number after the decimal point.
   The one with the highest number is the largest:
   9 is bigger than 4, so 75.9 is the largest.

So **Andy** weighs the most.

You could also answer this by putting the numbers into size order, then reading off the largest one.

Practice Questions

1) Is 11.32 smaller or bigger than 11.42?

   ....

2) If Candice spends over £15 she gets free delivery. She spends £15.49. Is her delivery free?

   ....

3) Vehicles over 2.8 m tall can't go under a railway bridge. Joe's wagon is 2.84 m tall.
   Can he drive under the bridge?

   ....

4) Put these numbers in order starting with the smallest: 6.2, 7.9, 3.4, 7.8

   ....

5) Baz can lift 85.6 kg, Kali can lift 85.9 kg and Dan can lift 85.3 kg. Who can lift the most?

   ....

6) Flynn has £212.56, Aadi has £209.13 and Oliver has £212.59. Who has the most money?

   ....

Fractions

Fractions Show Parts of Things

1) If something is divided up into equal parts, you can show it as a fraction.

2) There are two bits to every fraction:

The bottom number shows how many parts there are in total. → $\dfrac{3}{5}$ ← The top number shows how many parts you're talking about.

Fractions can be written in a few slightly different ways. For example, $\frac{3}{5}$ can also be written as 3/5 or ³/₅.

EXAMPLE 1:

Colin has 4 pieces of cake. He eats 1 piece. What fraction did he eat?

He's eaten 1 out of the 4 pieces, so it's $\frac{1}{4}$ (you say 'one quarter').

EXAMPLE 2:

Betty takes $\frac{1}{3}$ of the pens from a pack. What fraction of the pens are left?

A full pack contains 3 thirds. If she takes 1 third, then there must be 2 thirds left. So the fraction that's left is $\frac{2}{3}$.

How to Write Fractions

Here's how to write some common fractions:

One half = $\frac{1}{2}$ One quarter = $\frac{1}{4}$ Three quarters = $\frac{3}{4}$

One third = $\frac{1}{3}$ One fifth = $\frac{1}{5}$ One tenth = $\frac{1}{10}$

Practice Questions

1) Becca has 2 cans of pop. She drinks 1. What fraction of the cans did Becca drink?

$\frac{1}{2}$

2) Cliff had 10 desk calendars. He gave 3 away.

a) How many calendars does he have left? 7

b) What fraction of calendars does he have left?

$\frac{7}{10}$

Fractions Show Divisions

1) $\frac{3}{4}$ is another way of writing $3 \div 4$.

2) So you can type fractions into your calculator by dividing the top by the bottom.

3) This turns them into decimals.

> **EXAMPLE:**
>
> What is $\frac{3}{5}$ as a decimal?
>
> $\frac{3}{5}$ is the same as $3 \div 5$. So the calculation you need to do is: $3 \div 5 = \mathbf{0.6}$.
>
>

4) Here's what some common fractions are when written as decimals:

One half = $\frac{1}{2}$ = 0.5	One quarter = $\frac{1}{4}$ = 0.25	Three quarters = $\frac{3}{4}$ = 0.75
	One fifth = $\frac{1}{5}$ = 0.2	One tenth = $\frac{1}{10}$ = 0.1

'Of' means 'times'

1) Sometimes, you might need to calculate a 'fraction of' something.

2) In these cases, 'of' means 'times' (multiply).

> **EXAMPLE:**
>
> What is $\frac{3}{4}$ of £200?
>
> 'Of' means 'times' (×), so $\frac{3}{4}$ of £200 is the same as $\frac{3}{4} \times £200$.
>
> The overall calculation you need to do is: $3 \div 4 \times 200 = \mathbf{£150}$
>
>

Equivalent Fractions

1) Equivalent fractions are equal in size, but the numbers on the top and bottom are different.

$$\frac{1}{2} = \quad\quad \frac{2}{4} = $$

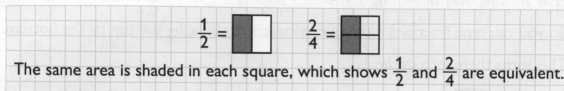

The same area is shaded in each square, which shows $\frac{1}{2}$ and $\frac{2}{4}$ are equivalent.

2) To get from one fraction to an equivalent one, multiply or divide the top and the bottom by the same number.

EXAMPLE 1:

Are $\frac{1}{5}$ and $\frac{4}{20}$ equivalent?

You can get from one fraction to the other by multiplying the top and bottom by 4, so they **are equivalent**.

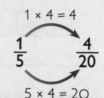

$1 \times 4 = 4$

$$\frac{1}{5} \quad \frac{4}{20}$$

$5 \times 4 = 20$

You can use a calculator to check they are equivalent —
$1 \div 5 = 0.2$ and
$4 \div 20 = 0.2$

EXAMPLE 2:

Which of the fractions on the right is equivalent to $\frac{6}{10}$? $\quad \frac{1}{6} \quad \frac{3}{5} \quad \frac{2}{3} \quad \frac{6}{20}$

Look at the top numbers to see what you have to multiply by to get from one to the other. Then multiply the bottom by the same number.

$$\overset{\times 6}{\frac{1}{6} = \frac{6}{36}} \quad \overset{\times 2}{\frac{3}{5} = \frac{6}{10}} \quad \overset{\times 3}{\frac{2}{3} = \frac{6}{9}} \quad \overset{\times 1}{\frac{6}{20} = \frac{6}{20}}$$
$$\underset{\times 6}{} \quad \underset{\times 2}{} \quad \underset{\times 3}{} \quad \underset{\times 1}{}$$

So $\frac{6}{10}$ is equivalent to $\frac{3}{5}$.

Ordering Fractions

1) Fractions are just numbers, so they can be put in order of size like any other numbers.

2) If the bottom number is the same, order them by the top number. If the top numbers are all 1, then a bigger number on the bottom means the fraction is smaller.

3) From smallest to biggest: $\frac{1}{10} \longrightarrow \frac{1}{5} \longrightarrow \frac{1}{4} \longrightarrow \frac{1}{2} \longrightarrow 1$

4) Here it is on a number line:

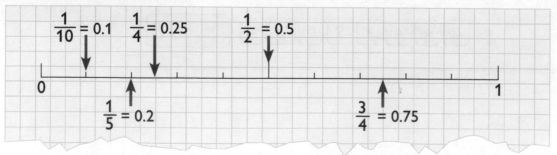

$\frac{1}{10} = 0.1 \quad \frac{1}{4} = 0.25 \quad \frac{1}{2} = 0.5$

$0 \qquad\qquad\qquad\qquad\qquad\qquad\qquad\qquad 1$

$\frac{1}{5} = 0.2 \qquad\qquad\qquad\qquad \frac{3}{4} = 0.75$

An office is buying some computers from either X-traComp Computers or Ultravision Computers. The computers cost the same price but X-traComp will give them $\frac{1}{2}$ off and Ultravision will give them $\frac{1}{3}$ off.

Who should they buy the computers from? Give a reason for your answer.

$\frac{1}{2}$ (0.5) is bigger than $\frac{1}{3}$ (0.33).

So they should buy them from **X-traComp** as they will be cheaper.

Practice Questions

1) What is $\frac{3}{4}$ written as a decimal?

_3.4_

2) Put the following fractions in order from smallest to largest.

a) $\frac{1}{8}, \frac{7}{8}, \frac{4}{8}, \frac{3}{8}$

$\frac{1}{8}, \frac{3}{8}, \frac{4}{8}, \frac{7}{8}$

b) $\frac{1}{5}, \frac{1}{10}, \frac{1}{2}, \frac{1}{20}$

$\frac{1}{2}, \frac{1}{5}, \frac{1}{10}, \frac{1}{20}$

3) What is $\frac{1}{5}$ of 450?

22.5

4) Are $\frac{7}{21}$ and $\frac{1}{3}$ equivalent fractions?

no ther not a eguivalen Fraction

5) Felicity has £560 to spend on her two week holiday. She thinks she'll spend $\frac{1}{2}$ of the money each week. How much money does she think she will spend each week?

6) Trisha and Hiram are reading the same book. Trisha has read $\frac{3}{4}$ of the book and Hiram has read $\frac{8}{12}$ of the book. Have they read the same amount?

Number Patterns

All Number Patterns have a Rule for the Next Number

1) Number patterns are lists of numbers that follow a pattern.

2) To describe the pattern you need to find the rule to get from one number to the next.

3) The rule often involves adding or subtracting an amount to a number to get the next number in the pattern. The amount you add or subtract stays the same each time.

4) To find the rule, you need to find the difference between each number and the next number along in the pattern.

EXAMPLE 1:

A number pattern starts 3, 7, 11, 15...
What is the rule to get from one number to the next?

To find the rule you need to look at the difference between each number and the next number in the pattern.

$$7 - 3 = 4, \qquad 11 - 7 = 4, \qquad 15 - 11 = 4$$

The difference is 4 and the numbers are getting bigger each time, so to get from one number to the next you need to **add 4**.

EXAMPLE 2:

A new fountain is designed so that each level is smaller than the previous one. The widths of the levels follow a pattern.

The first 4 widths (in inches) are 23, 21, 19, 17, 15...
What is the rule to get from one width to the next?

Look at the difference between each number and the next number in the pattern.

$$23 - 21 = 2, \qquad 21 - 19 = 2, \qquad 19 - 17 = 2, \qquad 17 - 15 = 2$$

The difference is 2 and the widths are getting smaller each time, so to get from one width to the next you need to **subtract 2 inches**.

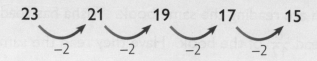

Follow the Rule to Find the Next Number in a Pattern

EXAMPLE:

A pattern starts 37, 31, 25, 19...
Find the next two numbers in the pattern.

1) First, find the rule connecting the numbers in the pattern.

$$37 - 31 = 6, \qquad 31 - 25 = 6, \qquad 25 - 19 = 6$$

The numbers are getting smaller each time, so the rule is **subtract 6**.

2) Then use the rule to find the next two numbers in the pattern.

$$19 - 6 = 13$$
$$13 - 6 = 7$$

So the next two numbers in the sequence are **13** and **7**.

Practice Questions

1) A sequence starts 5, 11, 17, 23, 29...
    What is the rule to get from one number to the next?

    ....

    ....

2) Mateo collects vinyl albums. The number he has at the end of every month follows a
    pattern. At the end of January he had 5 albums, at the end of February he had 9 albums,
    at the end of March he had 13 albums, and at the end of April he had 17 albums.
    How many albums will he have at the end of May?

    ....

    ....

3) James seals boxes in a factory. He counts how many boxes he has left to seal each minute
    and writes the number down. After four minutes, he has the pattern 67, 55, 43, 31...

    a) How many boxes does James seal every minute?

    ....

    b) How many boxes will James have left after 6 minutes?

    ....

Some Patterns Might Use Decimals

1) The method for finding numbers in a pattern with decimals is the same as for a pattern with whole numbers.

2) First find the rule that gets you from one number to the next number in the pattern — you'll be adding or subtracting a decimal amount.

3) Use the rule to find the next numbers in the pattern.

EXAMPLE 1:

A hardware store sells wooden planks. The widths of the planks follow a pattern.
The widths are 3.0 cm, 3.6 cm, 4.2 cm, 4.8 cm...
What are the widths of the next two planks?

1) To find the rule you need to look at the difference between each number and the next number in the pattern.

$$3.6 - 3.0 = 0.6 \text{ cm}$$
$$4.2 - 3.6 = 0.6 \text{ cm}$$
$$4.8 - 4.2 = 0.6 \text{ cm}$$

The numbers are getting bigger each time, so to get from one number to the next you need to **add 0.6 cm**.

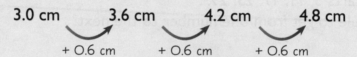

3.0 cm   3.6 cm   4.2 cm   4.8 cm
+ 0.6 cm   + 0.6 cm   + 0.6 cm

2) Then use the rule to find the next two sizes up.

$$4.8 + 0.6 = 5.4 \text{ cm}$$
$$5.4 + 0.6 = 6.0 \text{ cm}$$

So the widths of the next two planks are **5.4 cm** and **6.0 cm**.

EXAMPLE 2:

Lin measures the depth of a river every morning during a week in a dry summer. She notices that the depth changes in a pattern.

Her measurements for the first 4 days were 1.30 m, 1.14 m, 0.98 m, and 0.82 m.
What is the rule for the pattern in the river depth from day to day?

To find the rule, you need to look at the difference between the numbers.

$$1.30 - 1.14 = 0.16 \text{ m}, \qquad 1.14 - 0.98 = 0.16 \text{ m}, \qquad 0.98 - 0.82 = 0.16 \text{ m}$$

The numbers are getting smaller each time, so to get from one number to the next you need to subtract 0.16 m.

So the depth **decreases by 0.16 m** every day.

Practice Questions

1) Mia is training for a race. She tests herself by seeing how far she can run in 15 minutes.
   Over 4 weeks her distances are 2.5 km, 2.7 km, 2.9 km and 3.1 km.

   a) What is the rule for the pattern in her distances?

   ....

   ....

   b) Predict how far she will run after her 5th week of training using the pattern.

   ....

   Mia is also doing weight training to prepare for her race.
   In her first 3 weeks she lifts 27.4 kg, 31 kg, and then 34.6 kg

   c) What is the rule for the pattern in the weights?

   ....

   d) Predict how much she will lift after 4 weeks and after 5 weeks using the pattern.

   ....

   ....

2) A garage sells wheels which have widths that follow a pattern. The first three widths
   are 15.2 cm, 16.5 cm, and 17.8 cm. Wei needs a new wheel which is the next size up.
   What is the width of the wheel that Wei needs?

   ....

   ....

3) Gail is drinking water. She measures how much she has left after every 10 minutes.
   After 40 minutes she notices a pattern in how much water she has left.
   Her measurements are 0.87 L, 0.74 L, 0.61 L and 0.48 L.

   a) What is the rule for how much water Gail has left after every 10 minutes?

   ....

   b) Predict how much water Gail will have left after 1 hour (60 minutes) using the pattern.

   ....

Money

Pounds and Pence

1) If you get a question on money, the units will probably be pounds (£) or pence (p).

2) You need to be able to switch between using pounds and using pence.
   Remember that £1 = 100p.

> To go from pounds (£) to pence (p), multiply by 100.
>
> To go from pence (p) to pounds (£), divide by 100.

EXAMPLES:

1) What is £2.60 in pence?

Answer: You're going from pounds to pence, so multiply by 100.

$$£2.60 × 100 = \textbf{260p}$$

2) What is 70p in pounds?

Answer: You're going from pence to pounds, so divide by 100.

$$70p ÷ 100 = \textbf{£0.70}$$ ◄—— Correct money format is to write two numbers after the decimal point — so write £0.70, not £0.7.

Use Pounds OR Pence in Calculations — Not Both

1) You may get a question that uses pounds and pence.

2) If you do, you'll need to change the units so that they're all in pounds or all in pence.

EXAMPLE:

Cian buys a DVD online for £7.40. He pays 50p for postage.
How much has he spent in total?

1) Change the price of the postage from pence to pounds.

$$50p ÷ 100 = £0.50$$

2) Both prices are now in the same units (£).
   So add together the cost of the DVD and the postage.

$$£7.40 + £0.50 = £7.90$$

See page 32 for adding money using a calculator.

So Cian has spent **£7.90**.

Practice Questions

1) a) What is £3.84 in pence?

   handwritten: 0.0384   384p

   b) What is £1.27 in pence?

   handwritten: 0.0127 127p

2) a) What is 61p in pounds (£)?

   handwritten: 0.61

   b) What is 231p in pounds (£)? *handwritten: ÷ 231/100*

   handwritten: 2.31

3) Which is more expensive, a pen that costs 65p or one that costs £0.69?

   handwritten: 65p

Working with Money Without Using a Calculator

You might need to be able to solve money problems without using a calculator.

EXAMPLE 1:

Keiko is looking at two TVs in a shop. One costs £259 and the other costs £294. What is the price difference between the two TVs?

Answer: You need to subtract the smaller price from the larger one.

Price difference:
```
      8 14
   2 9̶ 4
 −  2 5 9
   0 3 5
```
So £294 − 259 = £35

See page 8 for how to subtract without using a calculator.

So there is a **£35** price difference between the two TVs.

EXAMPLE 2:

Keri buys two cakes for £4.
How much would it cost her to buy five cakes?

1) First, you need to work out how much one cake costs.
   You know that two cakes cost £4, so you need to divide £4 by 2.

   Cost of one cake: £4 ÷ 2 = £2

2) Now multiply the price of one cake by 5.

   Cost of five cakes: £2 × 5 = £10

So it would cost Keri **£10** to buy five cakes.

$$+ \begin{array}{r} 79 \\ 90 \\ \hline 169 \end{array}$$

Practice Questions

1) Grace has been shopping. She bought bread for 79p and milk for 90p.
    What was the total cost of her shopping? Give your answer in pence (p).

    ....

    O·87

    ....

2) James is buying some pet fish. He buys 4 angelfish for £20.
    How much would it cost him to buy 5 of these fish?

    ....

    ....

3) Lei is having a dinner party. She wants to spend £30 on food, £25 on drinks and £10 on
    decorations. She has an overall budget of £60. Can she afford to spend what she wants?

    ....

    yes she can afford the money

    ....

Adding or Subtracting Money Using a Calculator

1) You can add and subtract money using a calculator.

2) See page 9 for more on adding and subtracting using your calculator —
    just remember to type in the decimal point.

EXAMPLE 1:

Sooki wants to know how much she has spent on her shopping.

Potatoes £1.99

Cheese £2.99

Beans £0.59

Answer: add together everything Sooki has spent.

1.99 + 2.99 + 0.59 = **£5.57**

`1 . 9 9 + 2 . 9 9 + 0 . 5 9 =` `5.57`

EXAMPLE 2:

Sabrina would like to buy a newspaper for 99p and a drink for 55p.
She has £1.50 in her purse. Does she have enough money to buy both?

1) First, you need to add up the prices of the two things.

Total price: 99p + 55p = 154p

2) Change the total price into pounds: 154p ÷ 100 = £1.54

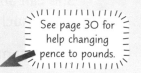

See page 30 for help changing pence to pounds.

The cost of the two things is £1.54. Sabrina has £1.50 in her purse.
£1.50 is less than £1.54, so **no** she doesn't have enough money to buy both.

Practice Questions

1) What is £1.99 + £2.99?

£ 4.08

+ £1.99
  £2.99

2) What is £15.99 − £10.50?

£5.49

  £15.99
− 10.50
  £15.49

3) Jamal is buying a box of cereal bars that cost £1.58.
He pays with a £5 note. How much change should he get?

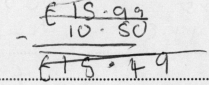

+ £1.58
  £5

4) Sonny gets £30 for his birthday. He spends £6.15 of this in a shop.
How much does he have left?

£23.85

  £30
− £6.15

5) Nicola is buying a shirt for £24.99. She has a gift token for £12.50.
How much does the shirt cost her?

6) Donald has a voucher for £2 off if he spends over £5 on fresh fruit.
So far he has bought kiwis for £1.55 and strawberries for £2.85.
Can he use his voucher?

Multiplying or Dividing Money Using a Calculator

You can multiply and divide money using a calculator in exactly the same way as whole numbers.

EXAMPLE:

Ami is saving up for a new radio.
She can afford to save £12.75 a month, for the next 10 months.
How much will she save in total in the next 10 months?

Answer: multiply the amount per month by the number of months.

$$12.75 \times 10 = \textbf{£127.50}$$

`1` `2` `.` `7` `5` `×` `1` `0` `=` `127.5` ←

Remember, money is always written with two numbers after the decimal point. So the answer is £127.50.

Practice Questions

1) What is £3.50 × 5?

   handwritten: 17·5

    *handwritten:* £3·50 × 5

2) What is £7.80 ÷ 10?

   handwritten: 0·78

    *handwritten:* £7·80 ÷ 10

3) Sanjay is buying sugar. 1 kg of sugar costs £0.69.
   How much will it cost to buy 5 kg of sugar?

4) Tim spends £36.75 on three books. Each book was the same price.
   How much did each book cost?

5) Fuel costs 124p per litre. Christie's car holds 50 litres of fuel.
   How much does it cost to fill Christie's car from empty? Give your answer in pounds (£).

Rounding to the Nearest £1

You might need to round amounts of money to the nearest pound (£).

1) Look at the number of pence in the amount (the digits after the decimal point).

2) If it's less than 50p, round down to the pound below — so £3.16 rounds down to £3.

3) If it's 50p or more, round up to the next pound — so £4.74 rounds up to £5.

EXAMPLE 1:

Ramesh is buying some material. It costs £2.32 per metre.
How much is this to the nearest pound?

Look at the number of pence in the amount. £2.32 means 2 pounds and 32p.

32p is less than 50p, so round down to the pound below.

The material costs **£2** per metre to the nearest pound.

EXAMPLE 2:

Some sweets cost £3.50 per kg.
How much do they cost to the nearest pound?

The number of pence is 50p, so round up to the next pound.

The sweets cost **£4** per kg to the nearest pound.

Rounding to the Nearest 10p

Sometimes you'll need to round to the nearest 10p.

1) Look at the last digit of the amount in pence.

2) If the last digit is less than 5p, round down to the 10p below — so 14p rounds down to 10p.

3) If the last digit is 5p or more, round up to the next 10p — so 47p rounds up to 50p.

EXAMPLE:

Kyle has 32p and Lila has 56p.
How much do they each have to the nearest 10p?

Kyle: The last digit of 32 is 2.
2p is less than 5p, so round down to the 10p below.
Kyle has **30p** to the nearest 10p.

Lila: The last digit of 56 is 6.
6p is more than 5p, so round up to the next 10p.
Lila has **60p** to the nearest 10p.

Estimating Money Calculations

You can use rounding to estimate answers to money questions.

EXAMPLE:

Carl is buying supplies on a company credit card.
So far he has spent £15.99, £13.99, and £127.99.
Estimate how much he has spent so far.

1) First round all the numbers to the nearest £.

£15.99 rounds up to £16.

£13.99 rounds up to £14.

£127.99 rounds up to £128.

2) Then add them together: 16 + 14 + 128 = £158

So Carl has spent about **£158** so far.

Practice Questions

1) Cheese costs £6.26 per kg. How much is this to the nearest pound (£)?

£6

2) A weekly saver bus ticket costs £15.75. How much is this to the nearest pound (£)?

£15.80

3) A packet of crisps costs 55p. How much is this to the nearest 10p?

60p

4) Petrol costs 124p per litre. How much is this to the nearest 10p?

130p

5) Entry to a zoo costs £14.50 for adults and £6.25 for children. Estimate how much it will cost for two adults and three children to go to the zoo.

6) Rahul is shopping. He buys food costing £1.99, £2.99, 99p, 99p and £3.99. He pays with a £20 note. Estimate how much change he'll get.

Time

Time Has Lots of Different Units

You need to be able to use lots of different units for time. You also need to be able to change between them. Here are how some of the units of time are related:

60 seconds = 1 minute	7 days = 1 week	10 years = 1 decade
60 minutes = 1 hour	365 days = 1 year	100 years = 1 century
24 hours = 1 day	12 months = 1 year	

15 minutes = a quarter of an hour

30 minutes = half an hour

45 minutes = three quarters of an hour

EXAMPLES:

1) How many seconds are there in 2 minutes?

There are 60 seconds in 1 minute, so to find out how many seconds there are in 2 minutes, you need to multiply 60 by 2:

60 × 2 = **120 seconds**

2) How many days is 48 hours?

1 day is the same as 24 hours, so to find out how many days there are in 48 hours, you need to divide 48 by 24:

48 ÷ 24 = **2 days**

Practice Questions

1) How many minutes are there in an hour and a half? ....*60 minutes*.............................

2) How many months are there in 2 years? ....*48 hours 24 months*..............

3) How many days are there in 3 weeks?
   21 days
   ....

The 12-Hour Clock and the 24-Hour Clock

1) You can give the time using the 12-hour clock or the 24-hour clock.

2) The 24-hour clock goes from 00:00 (midnight) to 23:59 (one minute before the next midnight).

> 06:00 is 6 o'clock in the morning. 18:00 is 6 o'clock in the evening.

3) The 12-hour clock goes from 12:00 am (midnight) to 11:59 am (one minute before noon), and then from 12:00 pm (noon) till 11:59 pm (one minute before midnight).

> 2:00 am is 2 o'clock in the morning. 2:00 pm is 2 o'clock in the afternoon.

4) For times in the afternoon, you need to add 12 hours to go from the 12-hour clock to the 24-hour clock. Take away 12 hours to go from the 24-hour clock to the 12-hour clock.

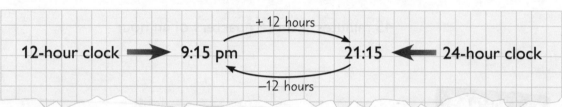

12-hour clock ➡ 9:15 pm + 12 hours / −12 hours 21:15 ⬅ 24-hour clock

Practice Questions

1) Change the times below from the 24-hour clock to the 12-hour clock.

   a) 10:30

   _22:30_

   b) 15:35

   _3:35_

2) Change the times below from the 12-hour clock to the 24-hour clock.

   a) 7:10 pm

   _19:10_

   b) 5:20 am

   _17_

3) Antony is meeting a friend at 9 pm. His watch reads 21:30 as he arrives. Is he late?

   yes of course Anthony late

4) A cinema is showing a film at these times: 18:55, 19:40, 20:10, 20:40 and 21:25.
   Sasha gets to the cinema at 8:05 pm. What is the earliest film she can watch?

   _20:10_

Reading Time from a Digital Clock

A digital clock displays time using the 24-hour clock.

08:23 = 08:23 (am)　　**11:59** = 11:59 (am)　　**23:47** = 23:47 (11:47 pm)

Reading Time from an Analogue Clock

An analogue clock displays time using the 12-hour clock.

1) The small hand shows the hour.

2) The big hand shows how many minutes past the hour.

   • It points to 12 on the hour (0 minutes past).

   • Every gap is another 5 minutes.

   For example, if the big hand is at 3, then it's 3 × 5 = 15 minutes past.

This is 10:15.
An analogue clock
doesn't tell you
if it's am or pm.

At 2:00 (or "2 o'clock")
the small hand is at 2.
The big hand is at 12.

At 2:15 (or "quarter past 2")
the small hand is just after 2.
The big hand is at 3.
3 × 5 = 15 minutes past.

At 2:30 (or "half past 2")
the small hand is half
way between 2 and 3.
The big hand is at 6.
6 × 5 = 30 minutes past.

At 2:45 (or "quarter to 3")
the small hand is just before 3.
The big hand is at 9.
9 × 5 = 45 minutes past.

3) You only say "past" until half past — so 2:10 is "ten past two".

4) After half past, you say "to" — so 2:50 is "ten to three",
   as there are 60 − 50 = 10 minutes until 3:00 (3 o'clock).

quarter past = 15 minutes past
half past = 30 minutes past
quarter to = 15 minutes to

EXAMPLE:

Vicky wakes up in the morning and looks at her clock.
She will be late for work if she wakes up after 8:15 am.
Will Vicky be late for work?

Answer:　The small hand is just after 8 but before 9.
　　　　　The big hand is at 2, so it's 2 × 5 = 10 minutes past.
　　　　　It's the morning, so the time is 8:10 am. 8:10 am is
　　　　　before 8:15 am, so Vicky **will not** be late for work.

Practice Question

1) What are the times shown below? Write your answers using the 12-hour clock.

a) Morning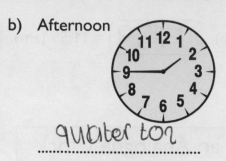

7:0clock

b) Afternoon

quater to2

c) Night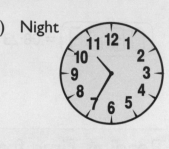

Working Out Lengths of Time

To work out how long something took, break it into parts.

EXAMPLE:

Nisha set off on a bike ride at 10:30 am and had a break at 12:25 pm.
How long had she been riding for?

10:30 am ⟶ 11:00 am ⟶ 12:00 pm ⟶ 12:25 pm
   30 mins   1 hour   25 mins

Add up the hours and minutes separately: 1 hour
     30 mins + 25 mins = 55 mins

So she was riding for **1 hour and 55 mins**.

Working Out Times

1) You may need to work out what time something will happen.
For example, when something will start or finish.

2) The best way to do this is to split the time into chunks.

EXAMPLE 1:

The time is 12:30 pm. Pete has a meeting in 45 minutes.
What time does the meeting start?

12:30 pm ⟶ 1:00 pm ⟶ 1:15 pm
  30 mins   15 mins

Split the time before the meeting into two chunks.
30 mins + 15 mins = 45 mins.

Pete's meeting starts at **1:15 pm**.

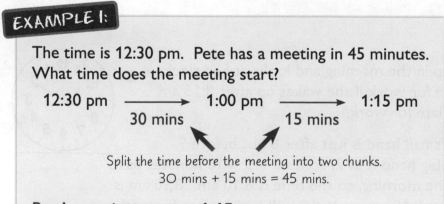

EXAMPLE 2:

Dianne is going to watch a film at the cinema. The film lasts for 1 hour and 30 minutes. During the film there will be a 15 minute break.

If the film starts at 7:30 pm, what time will it finish?

7:30 pm ⟶ 8:30 pm ⟶ 9:00 pm ⟶ 9:15 pm

1 hour   30 mins   15 mins

Film time   Break

It doesn't matter where in the film the break happens. The total time will be the same.

The film will finish at **9:15 pm**.

Practice Questions

1) A play starts at 7:00 pm and finishes at 9:30 pm. How long is the play?

   The play will be 2 hours

2) Pavel catches a train at 10:55 am and gets off at 11:50 am. How long was his journey?

   The Journey is 1 hour

3) An electricity company are planning a power cut. They will switch the power off at 5:15 am and turn it back on at 9:30 am. How long will the power cut last?

   The Power cut will last for 4 hours

4) Ben is going to a friend's house. His journey involves a half hour bus ride and then a 10 minute walk. If he gets on the bus at 6:00 pm, what time will he arrive?

5) Gary sets off for the gym at 18:55. It takes him 20 minutes to walk there. If he stays at the gym until it closes at 21:00, how long will Gary have spent in the gym?

   3 hours

Timetables Have Information About When Things Happen

1) Timetables have columns and rows.

2) Columns are the strips that go up and down.
   Rows are the strips that go across.

There's more about tables on page 75.

3) There are lots of different types of timetables —
   the best way to learn how to use them is to practise.

EXAMPLE 1:

The timetable below shows train times.
What time would you need to leave Preston to get to Deansgate for 12:30?

Preston	10:32	11:02	11:33	12:02
Buckshaw Parkway	10:44	11:14	11:45	12:14
Bolton	11:09	11:40	12:10	12:40
Deansgate	11:27	12:07	12:29	13:07

1) Find Deansgate in the timetable.

2) Follow that row until you reach the last time before 12:30. It's 12:29.

3) Go up the column till you reach the Preston row —
   this is the leaving time from Preston.

4) So you'd need to leave Preston at **11:33**.

EXAMPLE 2:

The timetable for a country show is shown below.

	Saturday	Sunday
10:00 am	Livestock show	Bakery judging
11:00 am	Woodland walk	Tractor show
1:30 pm	Butchery class	Birds of prey show
2:30 pm	Lawnmower racing	Sheep shearing
3:00 pm	Brass band contest	Celebrity chefs

1) What time does the tractor show start?
   Answer: **11:00 am** (on Sunday).

2) On which day is the butchery class?
   Answer: **Saturday**.

3) When is the birds of prey show?
   Answer: **1:30 pm on Sunday**.

Practice Questions

1) Debbie wants to travel by train from St David's to Topsham.

   a) If she wants to get there by 17:30, which train should she catch?

St David's	16:25	16:55	17:25
St James Park	16:29	17:01	17:29
Digby	16:33	17:07	17:33
Topsham	16:39	17:13	17:39

   ....

   b) She now needs to be there by 17:15 instead. Can she catch the same train from St David's?

   ....

2) Liam is going on a one day training course. His timetable for the day is shown below.

   a) What time does 'Reptile Care' start?

   13:30
   ....

Time	Activity
09:00 – 10:45	Introduction
10:45 – 11:00	Morning Break
11:00 – 12:45	Large Animal Care
12:45 – 13:30	Lunch
13:30 – 15:00	Reptile Care
15:00 – 15:30	Afternoon Break
15:30 – 17:00	Marine Animal Care

   b) How long is 'Large Animal Care'?

   ....

   c) Which is longer — morning break or afternoon break?

   ....

Calendars Show the Date

1) Calendars show all of the days, weeks and months in a year.

2) A calendar for the month of October is shown below.

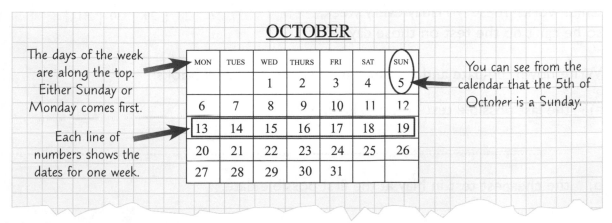

Working Out Dates Using a Calendar

You might be asked questions where you need to look at calendars and work out dates.

EXAMPLE:

Karen wants to go on holiday with her sister Ruth for a weekend in May. The calender shows the cost of flights.

(A weekend is Saturday to Sunday.)

- Karen can't go between the 1st and the 8th of May.

- Ruth can't go between the 25th and 31st of May.

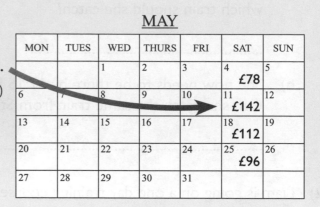

MAY

MON	TUES	WED	THURS	FRI	SAT	SUN
		1	2	3	4 £78	5
6	7	8	9	10	11 £142	12
13	14	15	16	17	18 £112	19
20	21	22	23	24	25 £96	26
27	28	29	30	31		

What is the cheapest weekend that the sisters could go on holiday together?

1) First, cross out any dates when the sisters can't go.

2) Next, look for a weekend when both sisters are available.

So the sisters could go on holiday on either the 11th-12th or 18th-19th.

The cheapest is the **18th-19th**.

MAY

MON	TUES	WED	THURS	FRI	SAT	SUN
~~1~~	~~2~~	~~3~~	~~4~~ £78	~~5~~
~~6~~	~~7~~	~~8~~	9	10	11 £142	12
13	14	15	16	17	18 £112	19
20	21	22	23	24	~~25~~ £96	~~26~~
~~27~~	~~28~~	~~29~~	~~30~~	~~31~~		

Practice Question

1) Chidi wants to book a driving test in May.

   Driving tests cost £62 on weekdays (Monday-Friday) and £75 on Saturdays.

   The test centre is closed on Sundays, and on the bank holidays on the 6th and 27th of May.

   Chidi works Tuesday-Friday every week, so he can't do the test on those days.

MAY

MON	TUES	WED	THURS	FRI	SAT	SUN
		1	2	3	4	5
6	7	8	9	10	11	12
13	14	15	16	17	18	19
20	21	22	23	24	25	26
27	28	29	30	31		

Write down the date and cost of the driving test if Chidi books:

a) the last possible test he can take in May,

....

b) the cheapest test in May at the first possible date.

....

Units

Everything You Measure Has Units

1) When you measure something you need to give the units.

2) Units tell you what type of number you've got. For example, you can't just say that a distance is 4 — you need to know if it's 4 metres or 4 miles.

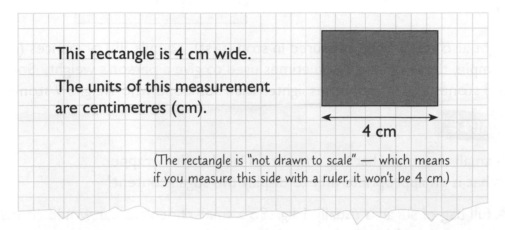

This rectangle is 4 cm wide.

The units of this measurement are centimetres (cm).

4 cm

(The rectangle is "not drawn to scale" — which means if you measure this side with a ruler, it won't be 4 cm.)

Units of Length

1) Length is how long something is.

2) Common units of length are:

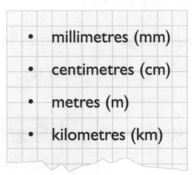

- millimetres (mm)

- centimetres (cm)

- metres (m)

- kilometres (km)

3) Here's how some of these units are related:

This means that 1 cm is the same as 10 mm.

Another way of saying this is that there are 10 mm in 1 cm.

Length
1 cm = 10 mm
1 m = 100 cm
1 km = 1000 m

4) You might also see length measured in miles, yards (yd), feet (ft) or inches (in). For example, these units are sometimes used to give someone's height. A person who is 5 feet 4 inches tall is shorter than a person who is 5 feet 9 inches tall. Distances on road signs in the UK are given in miles.

Units of Weight

1) Weight is how heavy something is.

2) Common units of weight are:
   - grams (g)
   - kilograms (kg)

3) Here's how these units are related:

Weight
1 kg = 1000 g

4) You might also see weight measured in stones (st), pounds (lb) or ounces (oz).
   For example, these units are sometimes used to give a person's weight. Someone who weighs 8 stones and 11 pounds is lighter than someone who weighs 9 stone 5 pounds.

EXAMPLE:

A small chocolate bar has a nutrition label on its wrapper.
What is an appropriate unit to display the sugar content?

A full bag of sugar is usually 1 kg. So a small chocolate bar would contain a lot less than 1 kg. So **grams (g)** would be an appropriate unit.

Units of Capacity

1) Capacity is how much something will hold.
   For example, how much liquid a jug will hold.

2) Common units of capacity are:
   - millilitres (ml)
   - litres (L)

3) Here's how these units are related:

Capacity
1 L = 1000 ml

4) You might also see capacity measured in pints (pt) or gallons (gal).
   For example, the capacity of a milk bottle is often measured in pints.

EXAMPLE:

Which of these items is most likely to have a capacity of 1.5 L:
a mug, a kettle or a bathtub?

A mug doesn't hold much liquid — usually less than 500 ml.
A kettle holds enough liquid to fill a few mugs — usually between 1 L and 2 L.
A bathtub holds a lot of liquid — usually over 100 L.

So a **kettle** is most likely to have a capacity of 1.5 L.

Practice Questions

1) Circle the units of length: metre   mile   millilitre

2) Circle the units of weight: centimetre   gram   ounce

3) Circle the units of capacity: millilitre   kilometre   gallon

4) Underline the units in the following sentences:

   a) An antique clock is 1.7 metres tall and 40 centimetres wide.

   b) A cardboard box weighs 200 g. When it's filled with books it weighs 14 kg.

   c) A barrel contains 35 gallons of oil.

5) How many metres are in a kilometre?

6) How many grams are in a kilogram?

7) How many millilitres are in a litre?

8) In the following pairs, circle the unit that is bigger.

   a) millimetre or centimetre

   b) kilometre or metre

   c) millilitre or litre

9) Fill in the table with an appropriate unit for each measurement.

Measurement	Unit
Weight of a dog	
Height of a person	
Capacity of a saucepan	
Length of an apple seed	

Length

Length is How Long Something is

You might have to answer questions where you have to do calculations with lengths.

EXAMPLE 1:

Colette has a 5 ft length of fabric. She buys another 0.5 ft long piece.
What is the total length of fabric Colette has now?

To find the total length, add together the lengths of the two pieces:

Total length = 5 ft + 0.5 ft = 5.5 ft

So Colette has **5.5 ft** of fabric.

EXAMPLE 2:

Matthew needs to paint a line halfway along a football pitch.
The pitch is 100 m long. Where should Matthew paint the line?

To find out where halfway along the pitch is, divide the length of the pitch by 2:

Halfway along the pitch = 100 m ÷ 2 = 50 m

So Matthew needs to paint the line at **50 m**.

Practice Questions

1) Fatima has covered 3 miles on her run. If she carries on for another 2 miles,
   how far will she have run in total?

....

2) Simon is painting his garden fence. The fence is 80 m long.
   So far, he has painted 45 m. How much does he have left to paint?

....

3) Andy has three planks of wood. Two planks are each 1.5 m long. One plank is 2.5 m long.
   What is the total length of all three planks?

....

Changing from One Unit to Another

1) If a number has units after it, then you can only add or take away another number with the same units.

2) So to answer some questions, you might need to change from one unit to another.

3) You can use the tables on pages 45 and 46 to help you change between different units.

This table will help you change between units of length:

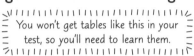
You won't get tables like this in your test, so you'll need to learn them.

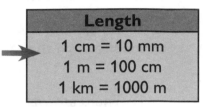

Length
1 cm = 10 mm
1 m = 100 cm
1 km = 1000 m

EXAMPLE:

Calvin's ladder is 2 m long. He extends it by 110 cm.
How long is the ladder now?

You need to add 110 cm to 2 m, but you can't because the units are different.

You first need to change one of the lengths so that they both have the same units.

You can see from the table that 1 m = 100 cm.
So to change m into cm you multiply by 100:

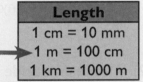

Length
1 cm = 10 mm
1 m = 100 cm
1 km = 1000 m

2 × 100 = 200 cm

Now the units are all the same (cm), you can add the two lengths together:

200 cm + 110 cm = 310 cm.

So Calvin's ladder is **310 cm** long when it's extended.

Practice Questions

1) Jacob is building a wall. It is 1.5 m high. He wants to add another 50 cm to the wall. How high will the wall be when Jacob has finished it?

....

....

2) Virginie is making a bracelet by putting beads on a string. Each bead is 5 mm wide. The string is 14 cm long. How many beads can Virginie fit on the string?

....

....

Section Two — Measures, Shape and Space

Comparing Lengths

Sometimes you might have to compare lengths (or widths, or heights).

EXAMPLES:

A basketball team is looking for a new player.

The heights of five possible players are shown in the table.

Player	Height
1	1.89 m
2	1.92 m
3	1.98 m
4	1.80 m
5	2.00 m

1) The team want a player who is at least 1.90 m tall. Which players could they choose?

   You need to look for players who are 1.90 m or more.

   • Player 1 is only 1.89 m, so is too small.

   • Player 4 is only 1.80 m, so is also too small.

   Players 2, **3** and **5** are all over 1.90 m. So the basketball team could choose any of these players.

2) The team decide to choose the tallest player they can. Which player should they choose?

   Player 5 is 2 m tall. This makes them the tallest player. So they should choose **player 5**.

Practice Question

1) Tony wants to buy a rug. The rug needs to be:

   • at least 1.8 m long

   • no longer than 2.7 m.

   Which of the following rugs could Tony choose?

Rug	1	2	3	4	5
Length	1.9 m	2.9 m	2.6 m	1.5 m	2.6 m

....

....

Weight

Weight is How Heavy Something is

You need to be able to solve problems involving weight.

EXAMPLE 1:

Aiden fills a box with books and board games.
The books weigh 4.5 kg. The board games weigh 2.5 kg.
The empty box weighs 0.2 kg. How much does the filled box weigh?

Add up the weights of the books, the board games and the empty box:

4.5 kg + 2.5 kg + 0.2 kg = 7.2 kg

So the filled box weighs **7.2 kg**.

EXAMPLE 2:

A sack of potatoes weighs 55 lb. Alan's trailer can carry a maximum of 600 lb.
He needs to transport 14 sacks of potatoes. Can he do this in one trip?

First, work out the weight of 14 sacks of potatoes.
To do this, multiply 55 lb by 14:

55 lb × 14 = 770 lb

770 lb is more than the maximum weight Alan's trailer can carry (600 lb).
So Alan **can't** transport all 14 sacks in one trip.

EXAMPLE 3:

Ellie buys a 1.5 kg bag of muesli. She buys a 450 g box of muesli too.
What is the total weight of muesli Ellie has bought?

First you need to change one of the weights, so they both have the same units.

Remember, 1 kg = 1000 g.
So to change kg to g you multiply by 1000.

1.5 × 1000 = 1500 g.

Now the units are all the same (g),
you can add the two weights together:

Weight
1 kg = 1000 g

This table is also on page 46.

1500 g + 450 g = 1950 g.

So the muesli weighs **1950 g** in total.

Practice Questions

1) Sunaira recently lost 11 lb in weight. Before this she weighed 178 lb.
   How much does she weigh now?

   ....

2) Paul needs to carry some bags to his car. Each bag weighs 5 kg.
   Paul can safely carry 20 kg in one go. How many bags can he carry in one go?

   ....

   ....

3) Harriet buys 1 kg of pasta. She uses 350 g for a recipe. How much does she have left?

   ....

   ....

Comparing Weights

It's often useful to compare the different weights of things.
For example, if you want to work out the heaviest or lightest thing in a group.

EXAMPLE 1:

Melissa, Shamilla and Jo need to find a fourth person for their rowing team.
The team can't weigh more than 228 kg in total.
The three of them currently weigh 167 kg.

Who should they ask to be their fourth member?

Person	Weight (kg)
Lucy	58
Rachel	68
Clare	62
Maryam	63

1) Work out the amount of weight they have
   left over for a fourth member:

   Weight left over = 228 kg − 167 kg = 61 kg

2) So the fourth member needs to weigh 61 kg or less.
   The only person in the table that weighs less than 61 kg is Lucy.

They should ask **Lucy** to be their fourth member.

EXAMPLE 2:

An airline allows each passenger up to three pieces of luggage.
The total weight of one person's luggage must not exceed 23 kg.

Alyssa and Steve want to take
these items on their holiday. ➡

Is it possible for Alyssa and Steve
to meet the airline's restrictions?

Item	Weight (kg)
Skiing Gear	19 kg
Suitcase	8 kg
Suitcase	7.5 kg
Camera Equipment	4.5 kg

1) Whoever takes the skiing gear would have 23 − 19 = 4 kg of allowed
weight remaining. This is not enough to take any of the other items.

2) There are 3 items remaining, with a total weight of 8 + 7.5 + 4.5 = 20 kg.

So **yes** it is possible to meet the airline's restrictions — Alyssa could take the
skiing gear and Steve could take the two suitcases and the camera equipment.

Practice Questions

1) Liz is going backpacking.
She wants to buy the lightest sleeping bag she can.
Look at the table.
Which sleeping bag should Liz buy?

Sleeping bag	Weight (g)
Sleep Right XV	1160
Comfort Pro VII	1400
Sleeper Light	800
Travelmaster 3000	1000

....

2) Dennis is on a low fat diet.
Which of the following sandwiches would be the best choice for his lunch?

Sandwich	Fat (g)
Chicken Mayonnaise	15.2
Tuna Mayonnaise	12.2
Ham and egg salad	13.5

....

3) Malik buys the following items at a supermarket:

Apples — 0.9 kg, Potatoes — 2.4 kg, Carrots — 1.5 kg

Use the pricing table below to write down the cost of each item.

Item	Less than 1.0 kg	1.0 kg-2.0 kg	More than 2.0 kg
Apples	£1.80	£3.60	£5.40
Potatoes	90p	£1.80	£2.70
Carrots	65p	£1.30	£1.95

Apples: £............................   Potatoes: £............................   Carrots: £............................

Capacity

Volume and Capacity

Volume is the amount of space something takes up.

Capacity is how much something will hold.

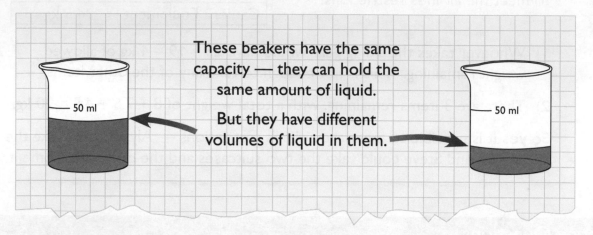

These beakers have the same capacity — they can hold the same amount of liquid.

But they have different volumes of liquid in them.

50 ml

50 ml

Questions on Capacity and Volume

You need to be able to answer questions involving capacity and volume.

EXAMPLE 1:

Jodie showers twice a day. Each shower uses about 45 litres of water. How much water does Jodie use showering each week?

Each day Jodie uses: 45 litres × 2 = 90 litres of water

In a week, Jodie uses 7 times this amount: 90 litres × 7 = 630 litres

So Jodie uses **630 litres** of water for showering each week.

EXAMPLE 2:

Mark is filling a 15 gallon fish tank using a 3 gallon bucket. How many full buckets of water will it take to fill the tank completely?

Divide the capacity of the tank by the capacity of the bucket.

15 ÷ 3 = 5

So **5 full buckets** of water would fill the tank.

EXAMPLE 3:

Gareth has made 5 L of stock.
How many 500 ml measuring jugs can he fill with the stock?

You need to divide 5 L by 500 ml, but you can't because the units are different.

So first you need to change one of the measurements so the units are the same.

Remember, 1 L = 1000 ml.
So to change L to ml you multiply by 1000.

$5 \times 1000 = 5000$ ml

Capacity
1 L = 1000 ml

Now the units are all the same (ml), you can divide the amount of stock by the capacity of a measuring jug.

5000 ml ÷ 500 ml = 10

So Gareth can fill **10 measuring jugs** with the stock.

Practice Questions

1) A 500 ml bottle is filled with 200 ml of water.

   a)   What is the capacity of the bottle? ....

   b)   What is the volume of water in the bottle? ....

2) Deepak has bought a fountain. It takes him three full 0.5 gallon buckets of water to fill it.
   How much water is in the fountain?

   ....

3) Catherine is going cycling with 3 friends. They take 2 L of water for each person.
   At the end of the day they have 0.8 L of water left. How much water have they drunk?

   ....

   ....

4) A jug is filled with 1 litre of orange juice. Four 200 ml glasses are poured from the jug.
   How much orange juice is left in the jug?

   ....

   ....

Comparing Volumes or Capacities

You might need to compare different volumes or capacities in your test.

Hannah uses about 4.5 L of water to water her vegetables.
Which watering can is the best for Hannah to use?

Watering can	Capacity
1	5 L
2	4 L
3	10 L

The capacity of watering can 2 is too low — 4 L is less than 4.5 L, so Hannah would need to fill the can more than once.

The capacity of watering can 3 is too big. It holds much more than Hannah needs. It'd probably be quite hard to carry.

Watering can 1 seems like the best one to use. It can hold 5 L of water. This is just over the 4.5 L Hannah needs to water her vegetables.

Practice Questions

1) Charlie is having a new hot water tank fitted in his guest house.
He wants it to have a capacity of over 160 L.

Hot water tank	Capacity
Duchess XL	150 L
Herald 175	175 L
Issigo ZF	130 L
AEB 224	165 L

Which of the tanks in the table above could he have fitted?

....

2) Sue wants to buy a small bottle of shampoo to take on holiday. The bottle can have a maximum capacity of 100 ml. She finds 3 bottles in the shop: 85 ml, 125 ml and 50 ml.

Sue wants to buy the biggest bottle she can. Which one should she buy?

....

Temperature

Temperature is How Hot or Cold it is

1) Temperature is a number that shows how hot or cold something is.

2) An object with a high temperature is warm or hot. For example, the inside of an oven.

3) An object with a low temperature is cool or cold. For example, the inside of a fridge.

4) Temperature can have different units.
   The most common are called degrees Celsius (°C).

- The temperature in a normal oven can reach around 230 °C.
- The temperature on a summer's day in the UK might be 26 °C.
- The temperature in a fridge is usually around 5 °C.
- Water turns to ice at 0 °C.

Calculations Involving Temperature

You might be asked to work out the difference between two temperatures.

EXAMPLE 1:

The temperature today is 17 °C.
Yesterday the temperature was 14 °C.

What is the difference in temperature between today and yesterday?

To find the difference, subtract the smaller temperature from the larger one.

17 °C – 14 °C = 3 °C

So the difference in temperature is **3 °C**.

EXAMPLE 2:

An oven is set to 180 °C. The temperature needs to increase by 35 °C.
How hot does the oven need to be?

Add the amount it needs to increase by to the current temperature:

180 °C + 35 °C = 215 °C

So the oven needs to be **215 °C**.

Comparing Different Temperatures

It is often useful to compare different temperatures.

EXAMPLE:

The Parker family want to go on a day trip to the coast.
The table shows the temperature forecast for 3 different places.

The Parkers want to visit the place that's likely to be warmest.
Where should they go?

	Temperature (°C)
Sandy Head	20
Minkie Bay	23
Port Anne	19

You need to find the place with the highest temperature in the table.
The table shows that Minkie Bay has the highest temperature (23 °C).

So the Parkers should visit **Minkie Bay**.

Practice Questions

1) Circle the highest temperature: 27 °C   38 °C   21 °C

2) Circle the lowest temperature: 2 °C   0 °C   5 °C

3) What temperature is 12 °C colder than 50 °C?

   ....

4) The temperature in Jeff's flat on Monday morning was 18.5 °C.
   On Tuesday morning it was 17 °C.

   a)   What is the difference in temperature between the two mornings?

   ....

   b)   On which morning was it warmest?

   ....

5) Jack has 3 recipes for biscuits. One says to set the oven to 200 °C,
   another says 190 °C and the final recipe says 225 °C. Jack decides to set the oven
   to the lowest temperature. Which temperature is this?

   ....

Scales

Scales are Used to Measure Things

1) A scale is something that you use to measure things.

2) Scales are found on things like rulers, kitchen scales, measuring jugs and thermometers.

Measuring Length

You can use the scale on a ruler to measure length.

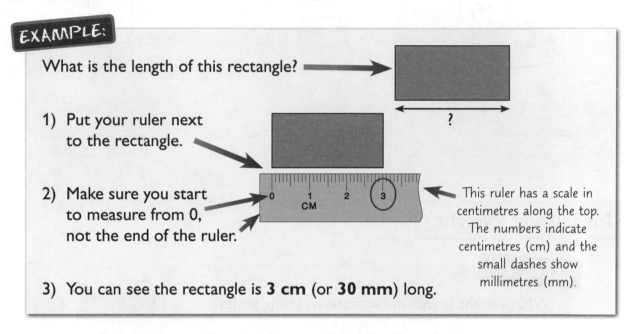

EXAMPLE:

What is the length of this rectangle?

?

1) Put your ruler next to the rectangle.

2) Make sure you start to measure from 0, not the end of the ruler.

This ruler has a scale in centimetres along the top. The numbers indicate centimetres (cm) and the small dashes show millimetres (mm).

3) You can see the rectangle is **3 cm** (or **30 mm**) long.

Measuring Volume

You can use the scale on a measuring cylinder to measure volume.

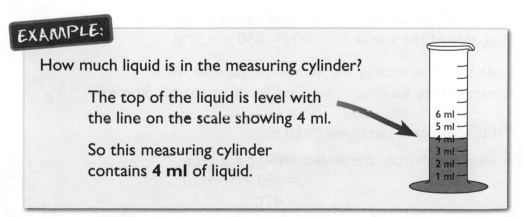

EXAMPLE:

How much liquid is in the measuring cylinder?

The top of the liquid is level with the line on the scale showing 4 ml.

So this measuring cylinder contains **4 ml** of liquid.

6 ml
5 ml
4 ml
3 ml
2 ml
1 ml

Practice Questions

1) Give the length of one side of the square on the right.

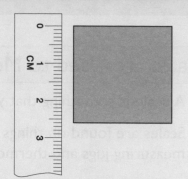

....

....

2) How much liquid is in each of the following containers?

a)

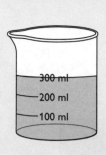

....

b)

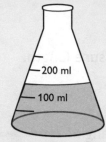

....

c)

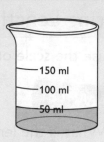

....

Measuring Weight

EXAMPLE:

What weight is shown on these weighing scales?

The arrow points to the weight in grams.

It points to a line with no number, so you'll need to work out what weight it's showing.

This g shows that the scales measure in grams (g).

To work this out:

1) Find the difference between the two numbered lines on either side of the arrow: 500 g – 450 g = 50 g

2) Divide the difference by the number of gaps between the two numbered lines. There are five gaps so: 50 g ÷ 5 = 10 g

So on this scale, each gap is worth 10 g.

So the weight shown on the scales = 450 g + 2 gaps
= 450 + 10 + 10
= **470 g**

Measuring Temperature

Another type of scale is the one seen on a thermometer.
By reading the scale you can work out the temperature.

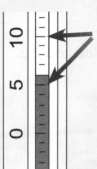

EXAMPLE:

Part of a thermometer is shown below.
It shows the temperature in °C. What temperature is it?

1) Find the difference between the two numbered lines: 10 − 5 = 5

2) Divide the difference by the number of gaps. There are five gaps so: 5 ÷ 5 = 1

3) So on this scale, the gap between each line is equal to 1 °C.

So the temperature = 5 °C + 1 gap
= 5 °C + 1 °C
= **6 °C**

Practice Questions

1) Every day, Akira records the temperature in her conservatory.
The thermometer on the right shows the temperature
one morning in °C.

What temperature is shown on the thermometer?

....

....

2) On the right is the dial from a set of weighing scales.

What is the weight shown?

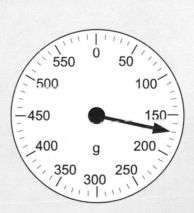

....

....

....

Angles

Angles Tell You the Size of a Corner

1) This is an angle.

2) Angles can be big or small.

3) Smaller angles are sharp and pointy. Bigger angles are wide and flat.

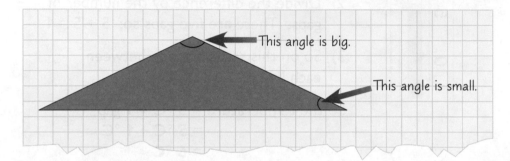

This angle is big.

This angle is small.

4) A right angle is a special type of angle. A right angle looks like this:

5) To spot a right angle, look for a square corner.

Practice Questions

1) Which angle is bigger, A or B?

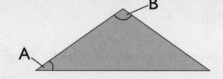

....

2) Write down the number of right angles in the following shapes.

a)

b)

c)

....

Lines of Symmetry

Some Shapes Have a Line of Symmetry

1) You can find out whether a shape has a line of symmetry by folding it in half.

2) If the sides fold together exactly, then the fold is a line of symmetry.

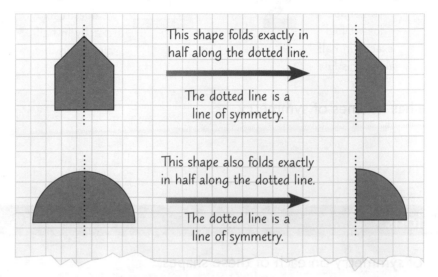

This shape folds exactly in half along the dotted line.

The dotted line is a line of symmetry.

This shape also folds exactly in half along the dotted line.

The dotted line is a line of symmetry.

Some Shapes Have More Than One Line of Symmetry

Some shapes have two or more lines of symmetry.

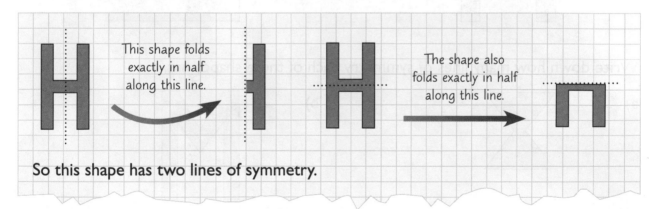

This shape folds exactly in half along this line.

The shape also folds exactly in half along this line.

So this shape has two lines of symmetry.

Lines of symmetry can go up and down, left to right or corner to corner.

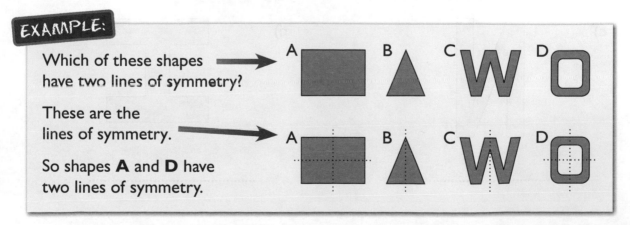

EXAMPLE:

Which of these shapes have two lines of symmetry?

These are the lines of symmetry.

So shapes **A** and **D** have two lines of symmetry.

A   B   C W   D O

A   B   C W   D O

Section Two — Measures, Shape and Space

Some Shapes Have No Lines of Symmetry

Some shapes won't fold exactly in half, no matter where you fold them.

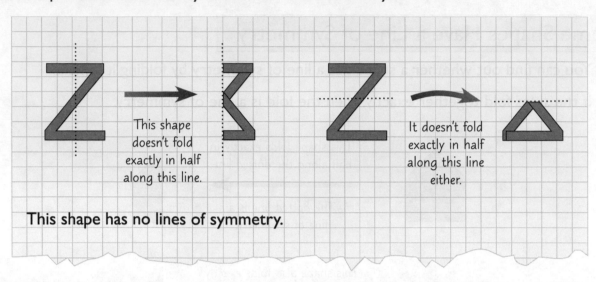

This shape doesn't fold exactly in half along this line.

It doesn't fold exactly in half along this line either.

This shape has no lines of symmetry.

Practice Questions

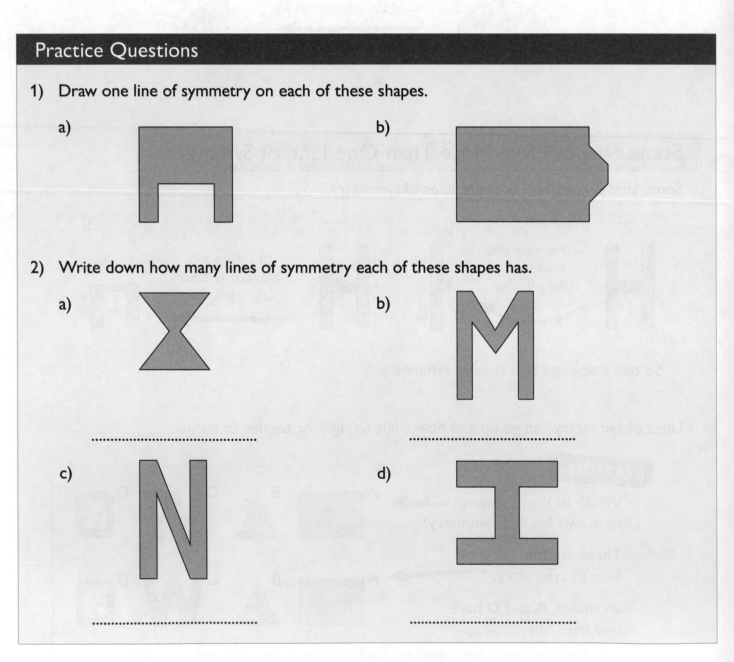

1) Draw one line of symmetry on each of these shapes.

   a)

   b)

2) Write down how many lines of symmetry each of these shapes has.

   a)

   ....

   b)

   ....

   c)

   ....

   d)

   ....

2D Shapes

2D Shapes are Flat

2D shapes are flat shapes — here are some examples.

A Square is a 2D Shape

1) Squares have four straight sides.

2) All the sides are the same length.

3) Squares also have four corners.

4) All the angles at the corners are right angles.

> A right angle is a square corner (see page 62).

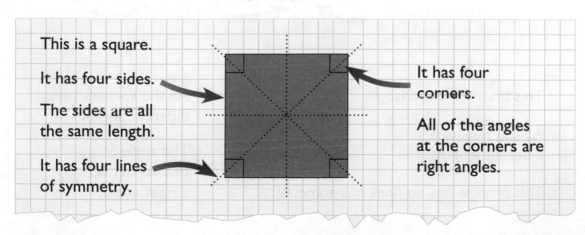

This is a square.

It has four sides.

The sides are all the same length.

It has four lines of symmetry.

It has four corners.

All of the angles at the corners are right angles.

Rectangles are 2D Shapes

1) Rectangles have four straight sides.

2) Sides that are opposite each other are the same length.

3) Rectangles also have four corners.

4) All the angles at the corners are right angles.

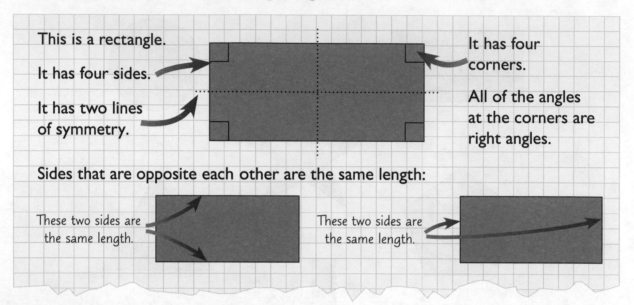

This is a rectangle.

It has four sides.

It has two lines of symmetry.

It has four corners.

All of the angles at the corners are right angles.

Sides that are opposite each other are the same length:

These two sides are the same length.

These two sides are the same length.

Triangles are 2D Shapes

1) Triangles have three straight sides. The sides can be different lengths.

2) Triangles also have three corners. The angles at the corners can be different sizes.

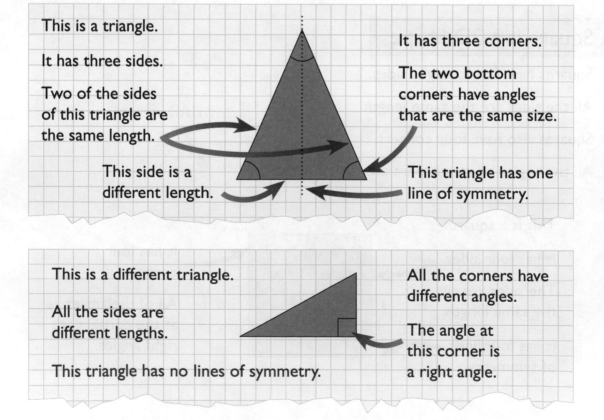

This is a triangle.

It has three sides.

Two of the sides of this triangle are the same length.

This side is a different length.

It has three corners.

The two bottom corners have angles that are the same size.

This triangle has one line of symmetry.

This is a different triangle.

All the sides are different lengths.

This triangle has no lines of symmetry.

All the corners have different angles.

The angle at this corner is a right angle.

Circles are 2D Shapes

1) Circles have one curved side.

2) They don't have any corners.

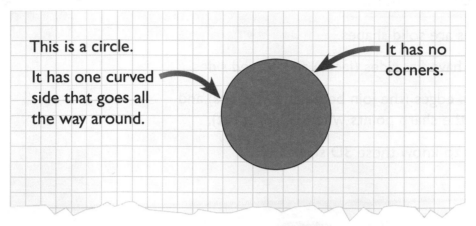

This is a circle.

It has one curved side that goes all the way around.

It has no corners.

Practice Questions

1) Name the following shapes.

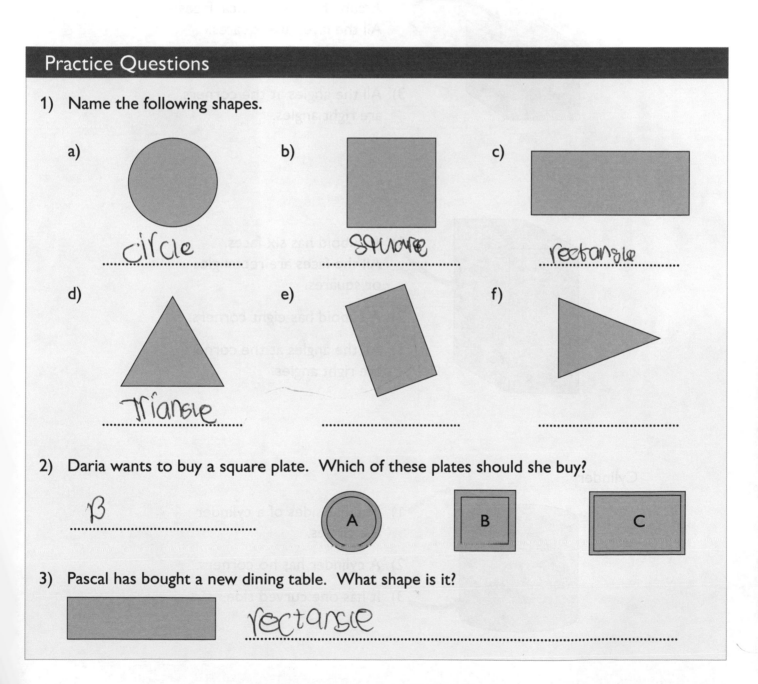

a) circle

b) square

c) rectangle

d) Triangle

e) ....

f) ....

2) Daria wants to buy a square plate. Which of these plates should she buy?

B ....

A   B   C

3) Pascal has bought a new dining table. What shape is it?

rectangle ....

3D Shapes

3D Shapes are Solid

1) 3D shapes are solid shapes.

2) They can have flat sides (faces) and curved sides.

3) They have edges (the join between two sides) and corners (the sharp points where edges meet).

4) You need to know these 3D shapes...

Cube

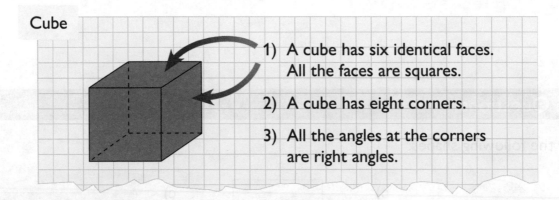

1) A cube has six identical faces. All the faces are squares.

2) A cube has eight corners.

3) All the angles at the corners are right angles.

Cuboid

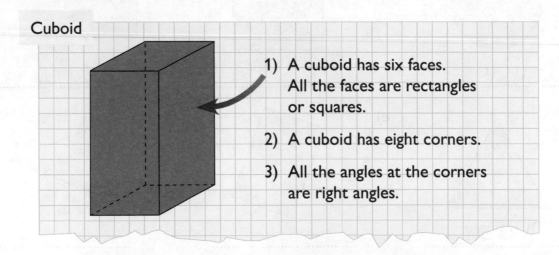

1) A cuboid has six faces. All the faces are rectangles or squares.

2) A cuboid has eight corners.

3) All the angles at the corners are right angles.

Cylinder

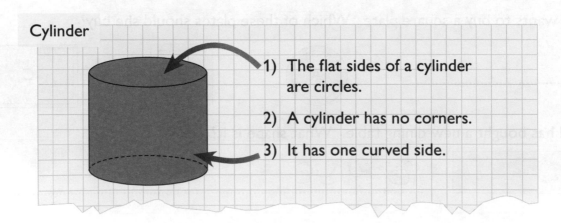

1) The flat sides of a cylinder are circles.

2) A cylinder has no corners.

3) It has one curved side.

Practice Questions

1) Name the following shapes.

   a)

   b)

   c)

   ....

2) Look at the sofa cushion on the right.
   What shape is it?

   Sofa cushion

   ....

3) Tracy wants a new coffee table. She wants it to be a cylinder.
   Which solid should she choose — A, B or C?

   A   B   C

   ....

4) Karim is using some modelling bricks.
   What two 3D shapes is this brick made up of?

   A .... and a ....

5) Each question part below describes a feature of a 3D shape. Choose which shape it is.

   a) Two of its faces are circles — is it a cube or a cylinder?

   ....

   b) The angle at each corner is a right angle — is it a cube or a cylinder?

   ....

Movement and Direction

Describing Movement

Movement can be described by talking about direction.

1) **Clockwise** — movement in the same direction as the hands of a clock.

2) **Anticlockwise** — movement in the opposite direction to the hands of a clock.

3) **Left** — movement towards the left.

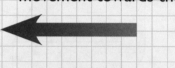

4) **Right** — movement towards the right.

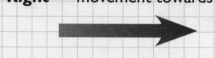

You can also talk about the amount of movement.

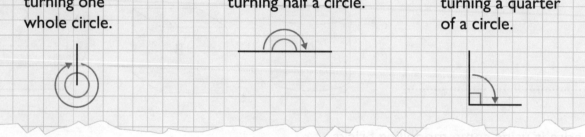

1) **Whole turn** — turning one whole circle.

2) **Half turn** — turning half a circle.

3) **Quarter turn** — turning a quarter of a circle.

EXAMPLE:

The dial on an oven is set to 0 °C.
The dial is turned half a turn to the right.

What temperature is the oven set to now?

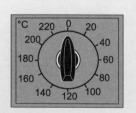

1) Half a turn means turning half a circle.

2) To the right is going this way: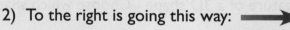

3) So the dial moves like this:

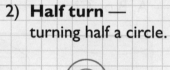

The oven is set to **120 °C**.

Practice Questions

1) The dial on an electric shower is set to Off.
   What is the dial set to if it is turned:

   a) a half turn clockwise?

   ....

   b) a quarter turn anticlockwise?

   ....

2) If the dial on the electric shower is set to Cold,
   describe how to turn the dial to set it to Hot.

   ....

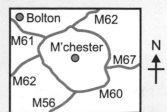

The Four-Point Compass

1) The four compass points are North, South, East and West.

2) Starting at North and going clockwise,
   the compass points always follow the same order.
   Use this rhyme to help you remember the order:

   Never (North), **Eat** (East), **Soggy** (South), **Wheat** (West).

3) You can use compass points to give directions.

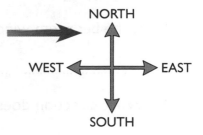

EXAMPLE:

Shrishti is going to Bolton. She's travelling north on the M56.
When she joins the M60, should she go east or west?

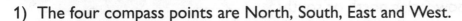

1) She's travelling north (up the page) on the M56.
   When she joins the M60 she needs to go to the left,
   towards the M61 and Bolton.

2) To work out whether left is east or west,
   fill in the missing compass points:

   Never (North), **Eat** (East), **Soggy** (South), **Wheat** (West).

   The compass should look like this: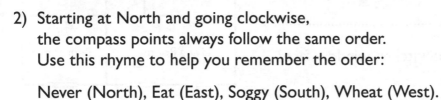

   So left is west.

   'N' on a compass means 'North'.
   'E' means 'East', 'S' means 'South'
   and 'W' means 'West'.

3) She should join the M60 going **west**.

The Eight-Point Compass

1) There are four extra compass points, making eight in total.
   The extra ones lie between the four main directions.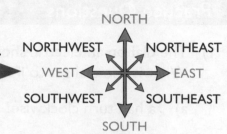

2) You can use all eight compass points
   to give more accurate directions.

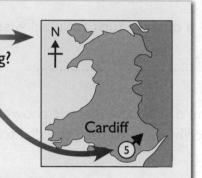

EXAMPLE:

Lloyd is watching a weather report. In what
direction is the wind arrow near Cardiff pointing?

1) The arrow is pointing up and to the right.

2) North is up, so right is east.

3) So up and to the right is **northeast**.

Practice Question

1) Trevor is buying a flat.

   a) Is the bedroom window facing north or south?

   ....

   b) What direction does the kitchen window face?

   ....

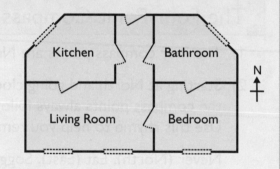

2) Look at the map of France.

   a) Is Paris east or west of Alençon?

   ....

   ....

   Marie lives southeast of Paris.
   She is driving to Alençon to visit a friend.

   b) Should she go clockwise or anticlockwise along the Paris ring road?

   ....

   c) Which direction should she head in from Le Mans?

   ....

Lists

Lists Can Be Used to Show Information

1) A list is a simple way of showing information.

2) Another word for information is data.

3) The data in a list can be in words, numbers or both.

---

1) A shopping list: ⟶   Bread, Milk, Tea, Biscuits

   This shows what you need to buy from the shops.

2) A price list for a hairdressers: ⟶

Wash and blow dry	£15
Cut and blow dry	£20
Cut and colour	£35

   This shows how much different services cost at a hairdressers.

Using the Information in Lists

You need to be able to use information from lists.

EXAMPLE 1:

This is the price list for a furniture store:

How much will it cost to buy the small bookcase and get it delivered?

Large bookcase	£50
Small bookcase	£45
Desk	£40
Delivery charge	£10

Answer:

1) Read down the list until you find the small bookcase. Then read across to find the price: £45

2) Read down the list until you find the word 'delivery'. Read across to find the price: £10

3) Now add the two prices together: £45 + £10 = £55

So it will cost **£55** to buy the small bookcase and get it delivered.

EXAMPLE 2:

Karen, Malia and Jo are arranging to meet up.
Jo makes a list of the dates when each of them is free.

Jo: 10th, 12th, 20th

Karen: 9th, 12th, 16th

Malia: 6th, 9th, 12th

What date are all three friends free to meet up?

Answer: look for a date that appears after each girl's name.

1) Start at the beginning of the list. The first date Jo is free is the 10th.

2) Now look at the dates after Karen's name. Karen is not free on the 10th. So the girls can't meet up on the 10th.

3) The next date Jo is free is the 12th.

4) Check the dates after Karen's name again. Karen is also free on the 12th.

5) Now check the dates after Malia's name. Malia is free on the 12th.

So all three friends are free to meet up on the **12th**.

Practice Questions

1) The list below shows the height of each person in group of friends.

   a) How tall is Faye?

   ....

Tina	1.45 m
Faye	1.8 m
Anika	1.6 m
Thom	2 m

   b) Who is the tallest?

   ....

2) Look at the menu on the right.

   a) How much will it cost to buy soup and a sandwich?

   ....

Tea cake	£1.10
Soup	£1.20
Sandwich	£1.60
Scone	£1.00

   b) How much more expensive is the tea cake than the scone?

   ....

Tables

Tables are a Way of Showing Information

Tables show information in columns and rows.

They're often easier to read than lists.

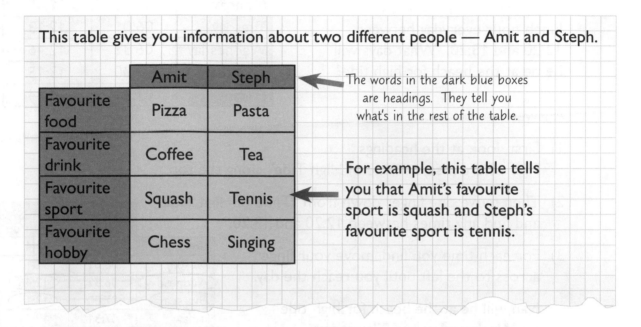

This table gives you information about two different people — Amit and Steph.

	Amit	Steph
Favourite food	Pizza	Pasta
Favourite drink	Coffee	Tea
Favourite sport	Squash	Tennis
Favourite hobby	Chess	Singing

The words in the dark blue boxes are headings. They tell you what's in the rest of the table.

For example, this table tells you that Amit's favourite sport is squash and Steph's favourite sport is tennis.

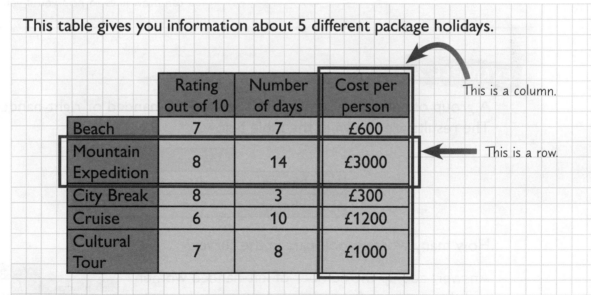

This table gives you information about 5 different package holidays.

	Rating out of 10	Number of days	Cost per person
Beach	7	7	£600
Mountain Expedition	8	14	£3000
City Break	8	3	£300
Cruise	6	10	£1200
Cultural Tour	7	8	£1000

This is a column.

This is a row.

Each row gives you all the information about one of the package holidays — you can see that the beach holiday has a rating of 7/10, lasts for 7 days and will cost £600 per person.

Each column gives you one piece of information (for example, the cost) about all of the different holidays. This means you can compare each piece of information — you can see that the most expensive holiday is the Mountain Expedition

Using the Information in Tables

You need to be able to use information in tables.

EXAMPLE 1:

The table shows the times of the low and high tides at a beach.

Ivan goes to the beach on his lunch hour everyday between 12:20 and 13:20. What days will he be at the beach for high tide?

	Time of Low Tide	Time of High Tide
Monday	05:32	11:45
Tuesday	06:01	12:13
Wednesday	06:32	12:46
Thursday	07:00	13:15
Friday	07:31	13:44

Answer:

1) First, look at the headings.
   Find where it says "Time of High Tide" along the top.

2) Then move one finger down from "Time of High Tide" and find any times between 12:20 and 13:20.

3) For each time you find, move your finger across to the left until you reach the day.

   Ivan will be at the beach for high tide on **Wednesday** and **Thursday**.

	Time of Low Tide	Time of High Tide
Monday	05:32	11:45
Tuesday	06:01	12:13
Wednesday	06:32	12:46
Thursday	07:00	13:15
Friday	07:31	13:44

You can draw lines to help you if you like.

EXAMPLE 2:

A group of people were asked if they were left-handed or right-handed. The results are shown in the table below.

	Women	Men
Left-handed	36	27
Right-handed	164	173

How many women took part in the survey?

Answer: add up the number of left-handed women and the number of right-handed women.

	Women	Men
Left-handed	36	27
Right-handed	164	173

36 + 164 = **200**

How many people were right-handed?

Answer: add up the number of right-handed women and the number of right-handed men.

	Women	Men
Left-handed	36	27
Right-handed	164	173

164 + 173 = **337**

Practice Questions

1) The table on the right shows the times of sunrise and sunset during a week.

	Time of Sunrise	Time of Sunset
Monday	07:01	19:08
Tuesday	07:03	19:07
Wednesday	07:04	19:05
Thursday	07:05	19:03
Friday	07:07	19:01

a) What time is sunrise on Tuesday?

....

b) Is sunset later on Wednesday or on Thursday?

....

2) A survey was done by a film club to find out people's favourite type of film. The results of the survey are shown in the table.

	Women	Men
Romance	57	43
Horror	20	40
Sci-fi	32	35
Action	66	57

a) How many men liked Horror films best?

....

b) How many women took part in the survey?

....

c) How many people said that Romance films were their favourite type of film?

....

d) Based on these results, what type of film should the film club show in order to please the most people?

....

3) Claire wants to buy a wedding present for her friend. Part of her friend's wedding list is shown in the table below.

	Price	Already bought
Wine glasses	£60	
Candles	£36	✔
Lamp shade	£40	
Salad bowl	£45	
Silver photo frame	£55	✔

The presents are quite expensive.
Some of them have already been bought by other people.

Claire wants to buy her friend the cheapest present she can, that hasn't already been bought. Which present should she choose?

....

Charts and Graphs

Tally Charts Help You Record What You've Counted

Tally charts are good if you need to count something.
For example, the number of different types of bird in a park.

1) Each line in the chart is called a tally mark.

2) In this case, you put 1 tally mark for 1 bird that has been seen.

3) To find out how many of each bird has been seen, count up the tally marks.

Type of bird	Tally
Robin	II
Blue tit	III
Sparrow	I
Pigeon	III
Seagull	IIII I

There are 2 robins.
There are 3 blue tits.
There is 1 sparrow.
There are 3 pigeons.
There are 6 seagulls.

In a tally, every 5th mark crosses a group of 4 like this: IIII
So IIII I means 6 (a group of 5 plus 1).

Frequency Tables Show How Many You've Counted

1) Frequency tables are like tally charts but they have an extra 'frequency' column.

2) Frequency just means 'how many', and a frequency table makes it easier to see how many there are in a certain category.

You can add another column to the tally chart above to make a frequency table.
You fill this in by counting up the tally marks for each bird.

Type of bird	Tally	Frequency
Robin	II	2
Blue tit	III	3
Sparrow	I	1
Pigeon	III	3
Seagull	IIII I	6
		Total: 15

Check the frequencies — the total should be the same as the number of tally marks (birds).

Drawing Tally Charts and Frequency Tables

1) To draw a frequency table you first need to draw a column with all the possible categories.

2) Then you need a 'tally' column where you count how many there are of each category.

3) Finally draw the frequency column and fill it in by counting the number of tally marks in each row.

4) Once you have finished your table you should check that you have all of the results by adding up all of your frequencies.

EXAMPLE:

10 friends are voting for which takeaway they should order from a choice of Chinese, Indian, Mexican and Thai.

Here are the results:

Nick — Thai	Sarah — Indian
Rikki — Indian	Yuan — Thai
Diego — Indian	Mark — Thai
Tom — Chinese	Mike — Thai
Helen — Mexican	Tamal — Thai

Draw a table to show this information.

The table will need space for all the takeaway options, each person's vote and the frequency of each option.

1) Each tally mark shows one person's vote. Cross off each piece of data as you record it to make sure you don't miss any or count any more than once.

2) You can check all the results have been tallied by looking at the total frequency — it should match the number of people asked (10).

Takeaway option	Tally	Frequency
Chinese	I	1
Indian	III	3
Mexican	I	1
Thai	ⅢⅡ	5
		Total: 10

The type of table you need depends on the information you need to display.

Practice Questions

1) A travel agent does a survey to find out what people's favourite type of holiday is.
   The travel agent collects people's answers in a tally chart.

Favourite type of holiday	Tally
Beach	IIII
Skiing	
Safari	IIII II
Cruise	IIII IIII
Sightseeing	IIII I

a) How many people said that a beach holiday was their favourite type of holiday?

....

b) Six people said that their favourite type of holiday was skiing.
   Fill this in on the tally chart.

c) What is the most popular type of holiday?

....

2) A groundsman is collecting information about the types of tree in a park.
   He writes down the type of every tree in the park.

pine	yew	yew	cedar	cedar
oak	beech	beech	oak	yew
cedar	beech	cedar	cedar	

a) Complete the frequency table below using the information above.

Type of tree	Tally	Frequency
Beech		
Oak		
Yew		
Cedar		
Pine		
	Total	

b) How many cedar trees are there?

....

c) How many oak trees are there?

....

Bar Charts Let You Compare Data

1) A bar chart is a simple way of showing data (information).

2) Data is shown on a bar chart as bars.

3) The height of each bar represents the frequency.

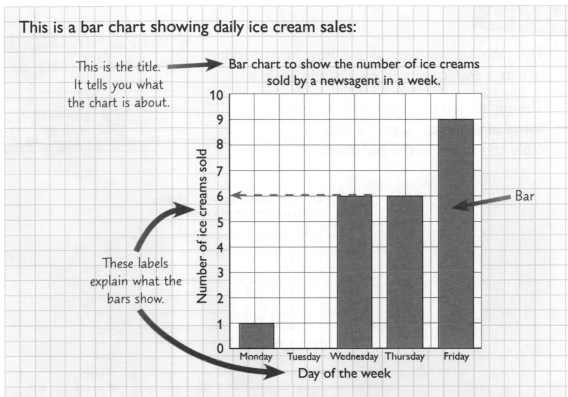

This is a bar chart showing daily ice cream sales:

This is the title. It tells you what the chart is about.

Bar chart to show the number of ice creams sold by a newsagent in a week.

These labels explain what the bars show.

Number of ice creams sold

Day of the week

Bar

1) The height of each bar shows how many ice creams were sold each day.

2) Just read across from the top of the bar to the number at the side.
   (You can draw a line if it helps.)

For example, on Wednesday, 6 ice creams were sold.

3) The tallest bar is on Friday. This means that more
   ice creams were sold on Friday than on any other day.

4) There is no bar on Tuesday.
   This means that no ice creams were sold on Tuesday.

5) The bars for Wednesday and Thursday are the same height.
   This means that the same number of ice creams
   were sold on Wednesday and Thursday.

Completing Bar Charts

1) You need to know how to represent data on a bar chart.

2) Use the frequency table to find how many things there
   are in the category you're drawing a bar for.

3) Draw a bar so that the height of the bar is equal to the frequency in the frequency table.

EXAMPLE:

The table on the right shows how many parking
tickets a traffic warden gave out in a week.

The unfinished bar chart below shows
some of the data. Use the data in the
table to complete the bar chart.

Day of the week	Number of tickets given out
Monday	22
Tuesday	18
Wednesday	8
Thursday	10
Friday	20

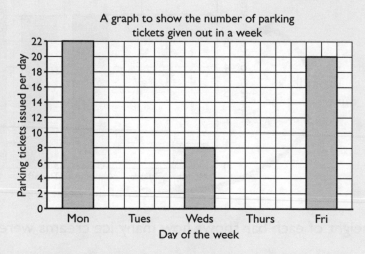

1) Use the scale on the left side to count up to the right number of tickets
   given out and put a mark at the correct heights.

2) You should draw a mark at **18** for Tuesday and a mark at **10** for Thursday.

3) Use a ruler to draw on the bars. Make sure that the bars you draw
   are the same width as the other bars, and that the gaps between
   the bars are all the same size.

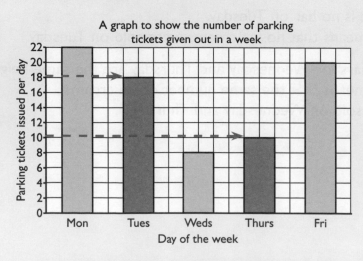

Practice Questions

1) Lisa does a survey to find out how people in her office get to work.

   The bar chart shows the results of Lisa's survey.

   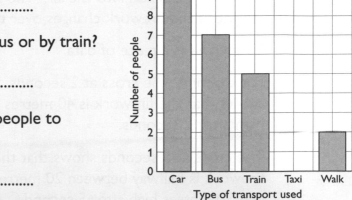

   a) How many people take a taxi to work?

   ....

   b) Do more people travel to work by bus or by train?

   ....

   c) What is the most common way for people to get to work?

   ....

   Lisa forgot to include the number of people who ride a bike to work on the bar chart.
   3 people ride a bike to work.

   d) How many more people ride a bike than walk?

   ....

2) A town council has built a new library. They asked local people how they felt about the library. The unfinished bar chart below shows some of the results.

   a) How many people said they were 'satisfied' with the new library?

   ....

   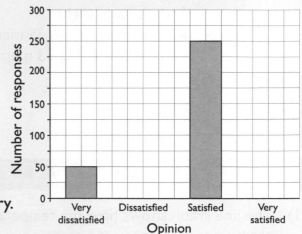

   b) 100 people who answered the survey said they were 'dissatisfied' with the new library. Add this bar to the chart.

   c) 125 people who answered the survey said they were 'very satisfied' with the new library. Add this bar to the chart.

   d) How many more people said that they were 'satisfied' than said they were 'very dissatisfied'?

   ....

   ....

Line Graphs Can Show How Things Change Over Time

1) Line graphs are useful for showing things that change over time. For example, distance or temperature.

2) Data is shown on a line graph as a line.

A firework is launched into the air. The line graph below shows how the height of the firework changes over time.

1) Each cross is a piece of data.

For example, the cross at 2 seconds shows that the firework is 40 metres high after 2 seconds.

The cross at 5 seconds shows that the firework is halfway between 20 metres and 30 metres high after 5 seconds. This means it is 25 metres high.

25 is halfway between 20 and 30.

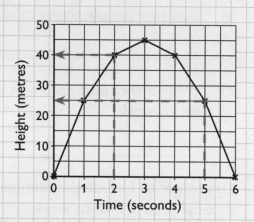

2) You can use the graph to estimate the height of the firework at any time up to 6 seconds. For example, to estimate the height of the firework at 4.5 seconds...

- Draw a line up to the graph from 4.5 seconds. (Halfway between 4 and 5.)

- Then draw a line across to find out the height. It's between 30 and 35 metres high — probably about 33 metres.

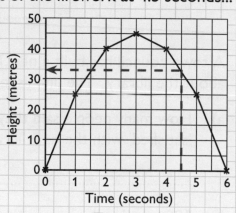

Practice Question

1) The line graph shows how the temperature in a garden changed during the morning.

a) What was the temperature at 8.00?

....

b) Estimate the temperature at 9.30.

....

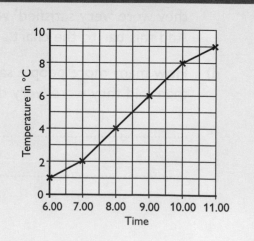

Completing Line Graphs

To complete a line graph you need to plot the points and then join each point to the next with a straight line.

EXAMPLE:

The speed of a rally car was measured every three seconds for 15 seconds. The speeds are shown in the table.
Plot the speeds on the grid below and join up the points to make a line graph.

Time (s)	Speed (mph)
0	0
3	35
6	65
9	90
12	105
15	115

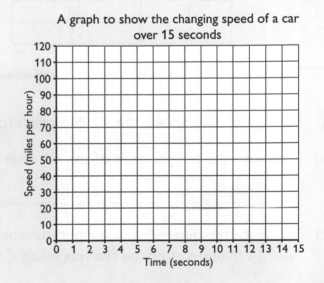

A graph to show the changing speed of a car over 15 seconds

1) Plot the points.

For example, at 3 seconds the speed was 35 mph. So start at the time (3 s) and move up until you reach the speed you want (35 mph) — draw a cross here.

2) Once you've plotted the points, join them with straight lines.

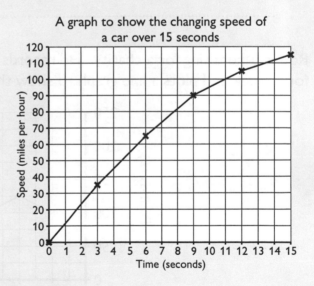

A graph to show the changing speed of a car over 15 seconds

Practice Questions

1) The table on the right shows the temperature of a cup of tea in the 20 minutes after it was made.

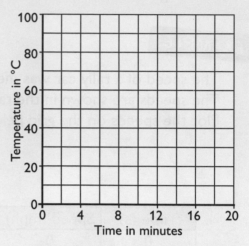

Time (min)	Temperature (°C)
0	95
4	70
8	50
12	40
16	30
20	25

a) Using the axes above, draw a line graph to show this data.

b) Estimate the temperature of the tea after 10 minutes.

....

c) Estimate the difference in temperature between 6 minutes and 14 minutes after the tea was made.

....

2) Rob is fundraising for a charity. He records how much money he makes each day for a week and plots a line graph to show the data.

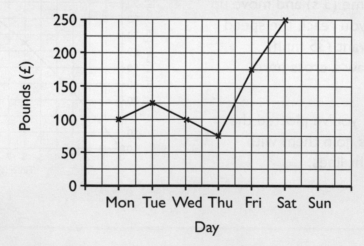

a) How much money did Rob make in total on Wednesday and Thursday?

....

b) Rob made £150 on Sunday. Use this information to complete the line graph.

....

Candidate Surname	Candidate Forename(s)

Test Date	Candidate Signature

Functional Skills

Mathematics   Entry Level 3

Section A — Non-calculator
Time allowed: 25 minutes

You **may not** use a calculator.

There are **9 marks** available for this section.

Section B — Calculator
Time allowed: 75 minutes

You **may** use a calculator.

There are **27 marks** available for this section.

You must have:
Pen, pencil, rubber, ruler, calculator (Section B only).

Instructions to candidates
- Use **black or blue ink** to write your answers.
- Write your name and the date in the spaces provided above.
- There are **2 sections** in this paper.
  Answer **all questions** in each section in the spaces provided.
- In calculations, show clearly how you worked out your answers.
- Check your working and answers.

Information for candidates
- The marks available are given in brackets at the end of each question.

Section A — Non-calculator

1   Arthur is hosting a dinner party.

He has a budget of £23 per person.

12 people in total will attend the party.

How much money does Arthur have to spend on the party?   (2)

Show your working and answer in this box.

£ _____

2   Arthur sends each guest an invitation.

> Party
> 7:45 pm Sunday
> Arthur's House

a)   **What time does the party start?**   (1)

Tick (✓) the correct answer in this box.

18:15 ( )   18:45 ( )   19:15 ( )   19:45 ( )

b)   **It takes one guest 30 minutes to get to Arthur's house. What time should they leave their house so that they arrive at 7:45 pm?**   (1)

Show your answer in this box.

_____ pm

3   Arthur is serving roast chicken for the main course.

How long to roast a chicken for			
Weight	Less than 1.4 kg	1.4 kg-1.6 kg	More than 1.6 kg
Time	85 minutes	105 minutes	125 minutes

He starts cooking a 1.52 kg chicken.

After 22 minutes in the oven, he takes the chicken out to check on it and then returns it to the oven.

How much longer does the chicken need to cook for?   (3)

Show your working and answer in this box.

_____ minutes

4 Arthur has a 750 ml bottle of pink lemonade for after dinner.

The pink lemonade is poured equally into 6 glasses, with none left over.

How much pink lemonade does Arthur pour into each glass?

Show your working and answer in this box.

_____ ml

End of Section A

Section B — Calculator

1   Felicia is driving to a car boot sale.

The diagram shows a roundabout on her route.

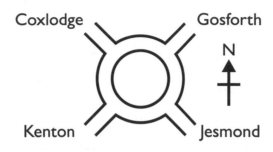

Felicia leaves the roundabout heading for Gosforth.

What direction is Felicia travelling when she exits the roundabout?   (1)

Tick (✓) the correct answer in this box.

East ( )   Northeast ( )   Southeast ( )   Northwest ( )

2   Felicia arrives at the car boot sale.

She enters the car park and sees that $\frac{1}{3}$ of the parking spots have been taken.

The diagram below shows the car park when it is empty.

Shade the diagram to show how many parking spots have been taken.   (1)

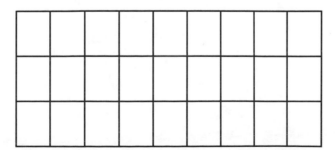

3 The car boot sale happens once every month.

The graph shows how many items Felicia sold in each of the past six months.

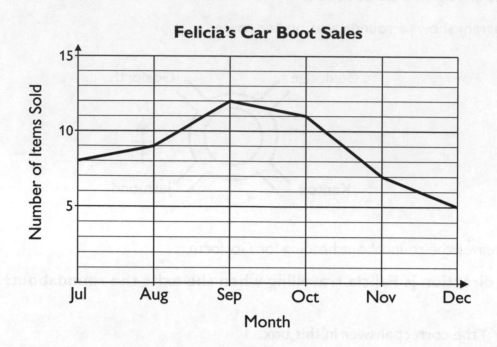

a) **How many items did Felicia sell in November?** (1)

Show your answer in this box.

b) **In which month did Felicia sell the greatest number of items?** (1)

Show your answer in this box.

4 Felicia displays her items on a table.

The diagram shows the size and shape of her table.

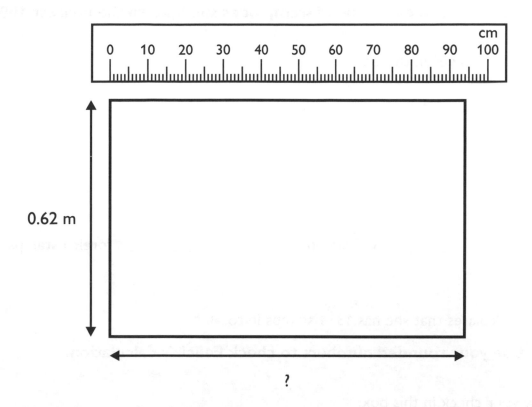

The maximum length of a table allowed at the car boot sale is 0.65 m.

Felicia's table has a length of 0.62 m.

a) Will Felicia's table be allowed? (1)

Tick (✓) the correct answer in this box.

Yes ( )   No ( )

b) Use the ruler in the diagram to measure the width of Felicia's table. Write your answer to the nearest centimetre. (1)

Show your answer in this box.

_____ cm

5 Felicia is selling her stamp collection.

She has 878 UK stamps and 436 foreign stamps.

a) **How many of each type of stamp does she have to the nearest 100?** (2)

Show your answer in this box.

_____ UK stamps   _____ foreign stamps

Felicia calculates that she has 1314 stamps in total.

b) **Use your rounded numbers to check Felicia's calculation.** (1)

Show your check in this box.

6   Felicia is selling this doll set. The heights of the dolls are shown below.

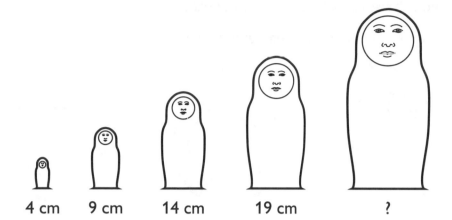

4 cm   9 cm   14 cm   19 cm   ?

The dolls' heights follow a pattern.

What is the height of the largest doll?   (1)

Show your working and answer in this box.

_____ cm

7 The car boot sale started at 8:00 am.

Felicia has been there for 1 hour and 45 minutes.

The diagram below shows three analogue clocks.

Clock A   Clock B   Clock C

Which clock shows Felicia the current time?

(2)

Show your working and answer in this box.

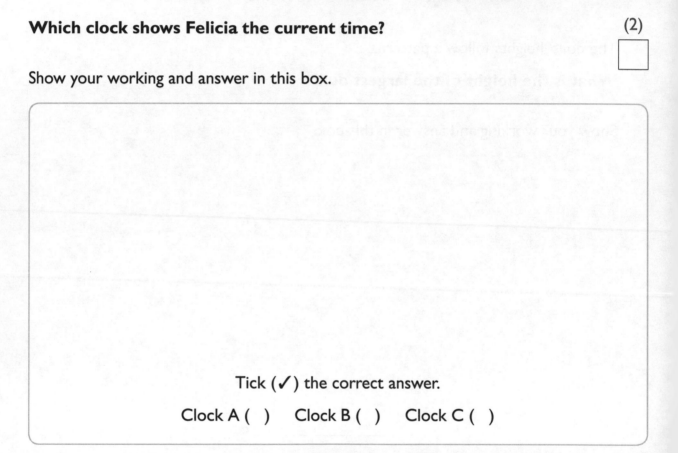

Tick (✓) the correct answer.

Clock A ( )   Clock B ( )   Clock C ( )

8   The stall next to Felicia is selling books.

Felicia writes down the type of each book.

These are the results.

Romance	Sci-Fi	Sci-Fi	Cookery	Romance
Horror	Biography	Cookery	Romance	Horror
Romance	Cookery	Romance	Cookery	Horror

a)   Complete this frequency table for the results.   (1)

Biography	1
Cookery	4
Horror	3
Romance	
Sci-Fi	2

Felicia notices that one of the books is out of place.

She turns the book so that it faces the same way as the others, as shown below.

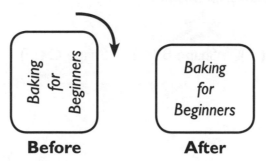

Before   **After**

b)   What fraction does Felicia turn the book?   (1)

Show your answer in this box.

9 Felicia snacks on some biscuits.

These are the shapes of her biscuits.

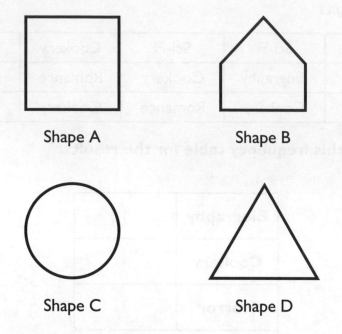

Shape A   Shape B

Shape C   Shape D

She chooses the shape with these properties:

- Fewer than four lines of symmetry.

- At least one right angle.

Which shape of biscuit does Felicia choose?   (1)

Tick (✓) the correct answer in this box.

Shape A ( )   Shape B ( )   Shape C ( )   Shade D ( )

10 Felicia has a flask of coffee to drink.

The temperature of the coffee was 67 °C at the beginning of the day.

The temperature of the coffee is now 42 °C.

How much cooler is the coffee now?

(1)

Show your answer in this box.

_____ °C

11 Felicia's flask holds 500 ml of coffee.

She pours 0.35 L of coffee into a cup.

How much coffee is left in the flask?

(2)

Show your working and answer in this box.

_____ ml

12 Felicia is handed a flyer.
The flyer gives information about how long some coffee cups take to biodegrade.

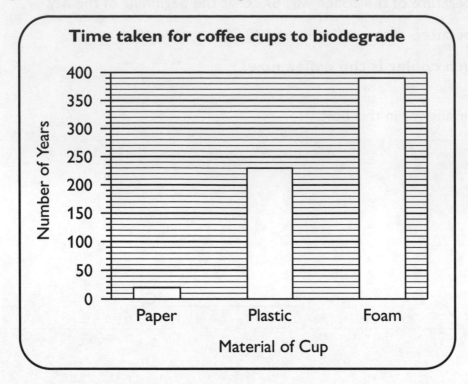

Felicia uses the information on the flyer and calculates that a foam cup
will take 160 years longer than a plastic cup to biodegrade.

Is Felicia correct?

(3)

Show your working and answer in this box.

Tick (✓) the correct answer.

Yes ( )   No ( )

13 Felicia buys three items: a travel mug, a teapot and a chest of drawers.

She weighs one of these items using mechanical scales.

Which item did Felicia weigh? (1)

Tick (✓) the correct answer in this box.

Travel Mug ( )   Teapot ( )   Chest of Drawers ( )

14 Felicia collects the money she makes in a container.

The diagram shows the shape of the container.

What is the name of this shape? (1)

Show your answer in this box.

15 Felicia counts how much money she has made.

She has sold £34.67 worth of items.

a) **How much is this to the nearest pound (£)?** (1)

Show your answer in this box.

£_____

Felicia sells another item for £5.03.

b) **How much money does Felicia have now?**
Use correct money format. (2)

Show your working and answer in this box.

16 Felicia has written down her sales for the day.

> Stamp Collection for £34 at 09:57
>
> Plastic Cup for £0.67 at 11:24
>
> Garden Plant for £5.03 at 12:35
>
> Doll Set for £17 at 13:03

She wants to show this information in a table.

Organise this information in a table.

(1)

Show your answer in this box.

End of Section B

Answers — Practice Questions

Section One — Number

Page 4
Q1 3

Q2 210

Q3 Dorothy (17 days)

Page 5
Q1 4, 7, 26, 27, 37, 129, 136

Q2 Heather, Rina, Katie, Sarah, Jane

Page 10
Q1 139

Q2 131

Q3 51

Q4 78

Q5 £17

Q6 405

Q7 17p

Q8 120

Q9 86

check: 86 − 49 = 37

or   86 − 37 = 49

Page 14
Q1 140

Q2 16 r 13

Q3 14

Q4 Yes (he has bought 70 screws)

Q5 a) 250

b) 750

Q6 6

Q7 336

Page 15
Q1 60

check: 60 ÷ 10 = 6

or   60 ÷ 6 = 10

Q2 25

check: 25 × 5 = 125

Q3 12

check: 8 × 11 = 88 (not enough)

8 × 12 = 96 (enough)

Page 17
Q1 a) 730

b) 700

Q2 600

Q3 a) 300 seconds

b) 290 seconds

Page 18
Q1 700

Q2 170

Q3 Estimate of change = £9

£10.05 is over a pound more than £9 so this suggests that she did not get the right change.

Q4 a) 30 + 30 = 60 marks,

so it looks like she did pass.

b) 61 is close to 60,

so Vashti is correct.

Page 21
Q1 Smaller

Q2 Yes

Q3 No

Q4 3.4, 6.2, 7.8, 7.9

Q5 Kali (85.9 kg)

Q6 Oliver (£212.59)

Page 22
Q1 $\frac{1}{2}$

Q2 a) 7

b) $\frac{7}{10}$

Page 25
Q1 0.75

Q2 a) $\frac{1}{8}, \frac{3}{8}, \frac{4}{8}, \frac{7}{8}$

b) $\frac{1}{20}, \frac{1}{10}, \frac{1}{5}, \frac{1}{2}$

Q3 90

Q4 Yes

Q5 £280

Q6 No

Page 27
Q1 Add 6

Q2 21

Q3 a) 12

b) 7

Page 29
Q1 a) Add 0.2 km

b) 3.3 km

c) Add 3.6 kg

d) 38.2 kg and 41.8 kg

Q2 19.1 cm

Q3 a) Subtract 0.13 L

b) 0.22 L

Section Two — Measures, Shape and Space

Page 31
Q1 a) 384p

b) 127p

Q2 a) £0.61

b) £2.31

Q3 A pen costing £0.69.

Page 32
Q1 169p

Q2 £25

Q3 No (she wants to spend £65).

Page 33
Q1 £4.98

Q2 £5.49

Q3 £3.42

Q4 £23.85

Q5 £12.49

Q6 No (he has only spent £4.40).

Page 34
Q1 £17.50

Q2 £0.78 (or 78p)

Q3 £3.45

Q4 £12.25

Q5 £62 (or £62.00)

Page 36

Q1 £6

Q2 £16

Q3 60p

Q4 120p

Q5 £15 × 2 = £30, £6 × 3 = £18
So total = £30 + £18 = £48

Q6 £20 – £2 – £3 – £1 – £1 – £4 = £9

Page 37

Q1 90 minutes

Q2 24 months

Q3 21 days

Page 38

Q1 a) 10:30 am
   b) 3:35 pm

Q2 a) 19:10
   b) 05:20

Q3 Yes, he is late (by 30 minutes).

Q4 20:10 (8:10 pm) is the earliest film
she can watch.

Page 40

Q1 a) 7:00 am
   b) 1:45 pm
   c) 10:35 pm

Page 41

Q1 2 and a half hours (or 2.5 hours
or 150 minutes)

Q2 55 minutes

Q3 4 hours and 15 minutes
(or 4.25 hours or 255 minutes)

Q4 6:40 pm (or 18:40)

Q5 1 hour and 45 minutes
(or 1.75 hours or 105 minutes)

Page 43

Q1 a) The 16:55 train.
   b) Yes, she can still catch the same
   train (it arrives before 17:15).

Q2 a) 13:30
   b) 1 hour and 45 minutes
   (or an hour and three quarters)
   c) Afternoon break

Page 44

Q1 a) Saturday 25th of May,
   cost = £75
   b) Monday 13th of May,
   cost = £62

Page 47

Q1 metre, mile

Q2 gram, ounce

Q3 millilitre, gallon

Q4 a) <u>metres</u> and <u>centimetres</u>
   b) g and <u>kg</u>
   c) <u>gallons</u>

Q5 1000 (m)

Q6 1000 (g)

Q7 1000 (ml)

Q8 a) centimetre
   b) kilometre
   c) litre

Q9

Measurement	Units
Weight of a dog	kg (kilograms) or st (stone)
Height of a person	m (metres) or ft (feet)
Capacity of a saucepan	L (litres) or pt (pints)
Length of an apple seed	mm (millimetres) or in (inches)

Page 48

Q1 5 miles

Q2 35 m

Q3 5.5 m

Page 49

Q1 200 cm (or 2 m)

Q2 28 beads

Page 50

Q1 Tony can choose from
rugs 1, 3 and 5.

Page 52

Q1 167 lb

Q2 4

Q3 650 g (or 0.65 kg)

Page 53

Q1 Sleeper Light

Q2 Tuna Mayonnaise

Q3 Apples: £1.80,
Potatoes: £2.70,
Carrots: £1.30

Page 55

Q1 a) 500 ml
   b) 200 ml

Q2 1.5 gal

Q3 7.2 L

Q4 200 ml (or 0.2 L)

Page 56

Q1 Herald 175 or AEB 224

Q2 85 ml

Page 58

Q1 38 °C

Q2 0 °C

Q3 38 °C

Q4 a) 1.5 °C
   b) Monday

Q5 190 °C

Page 60

Q1 2.6 cm (or 26 mm)

Q2 a) 300 ml
   b) 150 ml
   c) 50 ml

Page 61

Q1 7 °C

Q2 170 g

Page 62

Q1 B

Q2 a) 0
   b) 4
   c) 1

Page 64

Q1 a)

b)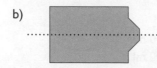

Q2 a) 2

b) 1

c) 0

d) 2

Page 67

Q1 a) circle

b) square

c) rectangle

d) triangle

e) rectangle

f) triangle

Q2 B

Q3 rectangle

Page 69

Q1 a) cylinder

b) cube

c) cuboid

Q2 cuboid

Q3 A

Q4 A cylinder (top) and a cube (bottom)

Q5 a) cylinder

b) cube

Page 71

Q1 a) Warm

b) Hot

Q2 A half turn clockwise (or a half turn anticlockwise)

Page 72

Q1 a) south

b) northwest

Q2 a) east

b) clockwise

c) northwest

Section Three — Handling Data

Page 74

Q1 a) 1.8 m

b) Thom

Q2 a) £2.80

b) £0.10 (or 10p)

Page 77

Q1 a) 07:03

b) Wednesday

Q2 a) 40

b) 175

c) 100

d) Action

Q3 Lamp shade

Page 80

Q1 a) 4

b)

Favourite type of holiday	Tally
Beach	IIII
Skiing	卌 I
Safari	卌 II
Cruise	卌 卌
Sightseeing	卌 I

c) Cruise

Q2 a)

Type of tree	Tally	Frequency
Beech	III	3
Oak	II	2
Yew	III	3
Cedar	IIII⁄	5
Pine	I	1
	Total	14

b) 5

c) 2

Page 83

Q1 a) 0

b) Bus

c) Car

d) 1

Q2 a) 250

b) and c)

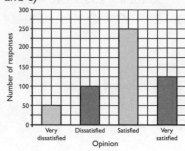

d) 200

Page 84

Q1 a) 4°C

b) 7°C

Page 86

Q1 a)

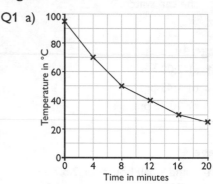

b) 45°C

c) 25°C

Q2 a) £175

b)

Answers — Practice Paper

Section A — Non-calculator (Page 88)

1
```
    2 3
  ×  1 2
    4 6
  2 3 0
  2 7 6
```
So 12 × £23 = **£276**.

(1 mark for a correct method to calculate 12 × 23, 1 mark for the correct answer)

2 a) 7:45 + 12 hours = **19:45** *(1 mark)*
   b) 7:45 pm − 30 minutes = **7:15 pm** *(1 mark)*

3 The chicken weighs 1.52 kg. This is in the range 1.4 kg-1.6 kg, so the chicken should be cooked for 105 minutes.
```
   ⁰₁¹0 5
  −   2 2
      8 3
```
So the chicken needs to cook for another **83 minutes**.

(1 mark for finding the correct time of 105 minutes from the table, 1 mark for a correct method to calculate 105 – 22, 1 mark for the correct answer)

4
```
      1 2 5
  6 | 7 ¹5 ³0
```
So 750 ml ÷ 6 = **125 ml**.

(1 mark for a correct method to calculate 750 ÷ 6, 1 mark for the correct answer)

Section B — Calculator (Page 91)

1 **Northeast** *(1 mark)*
   North is up, so east is right.
   The Gosforth exit is up and to the right, so it's northeast.

2 For example:

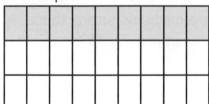

(1 mark)

There are three rows of parking spaces, each with an equal number of spaces. So it's easiest to shade the first row, as shown above. You'll get the mark as long as you shade any 9 spaces though.

3 a) **7 (items)** *(1 mark)*
   b) **September** *(1 mark)*

4 a) 0.62 m is less than 0.65 m, so **Yes** *(1 mark)*.
   b) **94 cm** *(1 mark)*
      Use the ruler in the diagram — each small division is 1 cm.

5 a) **900 UK stamps** *(1 mark)*
      400 foreign stamps *(1 mark)*
   b) **900 + 400 = 1300** *(1 mark)*

6 9 − 4 = 5 and 14 − 9 = 5, so the heights increase by 5 cm.
   So the height of the largest doll is
   19 cm + 5 cm = **24 cm** *(1 mark)*.

7 1 hour and 45 minutes after 8:00 am is 9:45 *(1 mark)*.
   The small hand should be between 9 and 10, but closer to 10. The big hand should be at 9.
   So **Clock C** *(1 mark)*.

8 a)
Biography	1
Cookery	4
Horror	3
Romance	**5** *(1 mark)*
Sci-Fi	2

   b) A **quarter turn** (or $\frac{1}{4}$ turn) *(1 mark)*

9 **Shape B** *(1 mark)*
   Shapes B and D have fewer than four lines of symmetry.
   Shapes A and B have at least one right angle.
   Only shape B has both properties.

10 67 °C − 42 °C = **25 °C** *(1 mark)*

11 1 L = 1000 ml, so 0.35 L = 350 ml *(1 mark)*
    500 ml − 350 ml = **150 ml** *(1 mark)*

12 The flyer says that plastic cups take 230 years to biodegrade and foam cups take 390 years to biodegrade.
    390 − 230 = 160 years
    So the answer is **Yes**.
    (1 mark for reading 230 and 390 off the graph, 1 mark for calculating 390 – 230, 1 mark for the correct answer)

13 **Chest of Drawers** *(1 mark)*
    The scale reads 43 kg — both a travel mug and potted plant would weigh less than this.

14 **Cylinder** *(1 mark)*

15 a) £34.67 = **£35** *(1 mark)* to the nearest pound.
    b) £34.67 + £5.03 = **£39.70**
       (1 mark for calculating 34.67 + 5.03, 1 mark for the correct answer in correct money format)
       You must write two digits after the decimal point when working with money — you would only get one mark for writing £39.7.

16 For example:

Sales Record		
Item	**Price**	**Time**
Stamp Collection	£34	09:57
Plastic Cup	£0.67	11:24
Garden Plant	£5.03	12:35
Doll Set	£17	13:03

(1 mark)

The table should have suitable headings (e.g. "Item", "Price (in £)" and "Time"). The data can be shown in columns (as above) or in rows. Each row/column must contain the correct values.

The £ sign may be in seen in the data heading or with each amount. The time can be written using either the 12-hour clock or the 24-hour clock.

A table without borders is acceptable.

Glossary

12-hour Clock

The 12 hour clock goes from 12:00 am (midnight) to 11:59 am (one minute before noon), and then from 12:00 pm (noon) till 11:59 pm (one minute before midnight).

24-hour Clock

The 24 hour clock goes from 00:00 (midnight) to 23:59 (one minute before the next midnight).

2D Shape

A flat shape.

3D Shape

A solid shape.

Angle

A measurement that tells you the size of a corner.

Anticlockwise

Movement in the opposite direction to the hands of a clock.

Bar Chart

A chart which shows information using bars.

Capacity

How much something will hold. For example, a beaker with a capacity of 200 ml can hold 200 ml of liquid.

Circle

A 2D shape with one curved side and no corners.

Clockwise

Movement in the same direction as the hands of a clock.

Compass Points

The directions of a compass. The four main directions are: North, East, South and West. The four extra directions which are added to make an eight-point compass are: Northeast, Southeast, Southwest and Northwest.

Cube

A 3D shape in which all the faces are squares.

Cuboid

A 3D shape in which all the faces are rectangles or squares.

Cylinder

A 3D shape in which the two flat faces are circles. A cylinder has no corners.

Data

Another word for information.

Decimal Number

A number with a decimal point (.) in it. For example, 0.75.

Digit

One of these: 0 1 2 3 4 5 6 7 8 9. All numbers are made by putting these digits together. For example: 22, 359.

Estimate

A close guess at what an answer will be.

Fraction

A way of showing parts of a whole. For example: ¼ (one quarter).

Frequency Table

A table showing the frequency of items (how many there are) in different categories.

Length

How long something is. It can be measured in different units, for example, millimetres (mm), centimetres (cm), or metres (m).

Line Graph

A graph which shows data using a line.

Line of Symmetry

A shape with a line of symmetry has two halves that are mirror images of each other. If the shape is folded along this line, the two sides will fold exactly together.

List

A simple way of showing information. For example, a shopping list shows what you need to buy from the shops.

Number Pattern

A list of numbers that follow a pattern.

Rectangle

A 2D shape with 4 sides. Sides that are opposite each other are the same length. The angles at the corners are all right angles.

Right angle

A square corner.

Scale

Something you use to measure things. For example, you can use the scale on a ruler to measure length.

Square

A 2D shape with 4 sides. All the sides are the same length. The angles at the corners are all right angles.

Symmetry

See line of symmetry.

Table

A way of showing data. In a table, data is arranged into columns and rows.

Tally Chart

A chart used for putting data into different categories. You use tally marks (lines) to record each piece of data in the chart.

Temperature

A number that shows how hot or cold something is. Degrees Celsius (°C) are common units for temperature.

Timetable

A table with information about when things will happen.

Triangle

A 2D shape with 3 straight sides and 3 corners.

Unit

A way of showing what type of number you've got. For example, metres (m) or grams (g).

Volume

The amount of space something takes up.

Weight

How heavy something is. Grams (g) and kilograms (kg) are common units for weight.

Index

M3FSRA1